PRACTICAL PIC
MICROCONTROLLER
PROJECTS

Other Titles of Interest

PRACTICAL PIC
MICROCONTROLLER
PROJECTS

by

R. A. PENFOLD

BERNARD BABANI (publishing) LTD
THE GRAMPIANS
SHEPHERDS BUSH ROAD
LONDON W6 7NF
ENGLAND

Please Note

Although every care has been taken with the production of this book to ensure that any projects, designs, modifications and/or programs, etc., contained herewith, operate in a correct and safe manner and also that any components specified are normally available in Great Britain, the Publishers do not accept responsibility in any way for the failure, including fault in design, of any project, design, modification or program to work correctly or to cause damage to any other equipment that it may be connected to or used in conjunction with, or in respect of any other damage or injury that may be so caused, nor do the Publishers accept responsibility in any way for the failure to obtain specified components.

Notice is also given that if equipment that is still under warranty is modified in any way or used or connected with home-built equipment then that warranty may be void.

First Published – February 1999

British Library Cataloguing in Publication Data

A catalogue record for this book is available from the British Library

ISBN 0 85934 444 4

Cover designed by Gregor Arthur

Printed and bound in Great Britain by Cox & Wyman Ltd, Reading

Preface

Every now and then a development that revolutionises electronic circuit design occurs. The latest of these is undoubtedly the introduction of low cost microcontrollers that are relatively easy to program and use, and run at very low power levels. A microcontroller is a complete but basic computer on a single chip. The single chip computer is by no means a new idea, but the early devices were quite complex, very expensive, and consumed high power levels. They were more or less, just the popular eight-bit processors of the day with added memory and ports. The high cost and power consumption of these devices rendered them unsuitable for many potential applications, and they failed to achieve widespread acceptance.

The new breed of microcontroller is a very different prospect. Their low cost makes them a practical alternative to conventional logic circuits in even the most basic of applications. They are also well suited to situations that require small battery powered devices. The PIC processors are the most popular family of microcontrollers at present, and they feature in a fair percentage of published electronic designs for the home constructor. Obviously PIC processors are not well suited to all applications. You can not connect a ferrite aerial to a PIC input, a loudspeaker to an output, and load the right software to make the circuit operate as an a.m. radio! On the other hand, some PIC processors have built-in analogue to digital converters, and any of them can be used with external digital to analogue converters. This enables PIC processors to be used in a wide range of analogue and digital applications.

This book covers a wide range of PIC based projects, including such things as digitally controlled power supplies, transistor checkers, a simple capacitance meter, reaction tester, digital dice, digital locks, a stereo audio level meter, and MIDI pedals for use with electronic music systems. No construction details are provided for the projects, but in most cases the circuits are very simple and they are easily constructed using stripboard, etc. Full component lists and software listings are provided, together with descriptions of the way in which the programs function. The reader is assumed to have a basic understanding of PIC microcontrollers, how they are programmed, etc. Newcomers to PIC processors need to learn the fundamentals of these devices prior to undertaking the projects in this book. "An Introduction to PIC Microcontrollers" (BP394) from the same publisher and author as this book gives you all the background information you will need.

R. A. Penfold

Contents

Page

Chapter 1

TEST GEAR

Pushbutton Power Supply (1)

When using a variable voltage bench power supply it is easy to make the mistake of switching on first and then setting the output voltage. In many cases this will not have any dire consequences, but there can be problems if you are using the unit to power a five volt logic circuit and the previous circuit used with the unit required 20 volts or so! Some variable voltage power supply units overcome this problem by having the output voltage always start at zero. Once the unit has been switched on you can then set the required output voltage. It is possible to achieve this start at zero operation using analogue circuitry, but it can be difficult to get adequate stability. The supply voltage tends to 'sag' after the unit has been in operation for some time. Digital control offers much greater stability and no problems at all with long term drifting of the output potential.

Two forms of digitally controlled power supply are featured here, and the first of these is operated by way of four pushbutton switches. Two switches are used to increase the output voltage and the other two are used to decrease it. The switches offer fast and slow control so that the output voltage can quickly be set to approximately the required potential, and then 'fine tuned' to precisely the required voltage. Output voltages from zero to 20 volts are available with a maximum output current of 1.4 amps. The output voltage is set with a resolution of 100 millivolts (0.1 volts).

The output noise level is well under one millivolt RMS at most output voltages. Potentials from 20 to 24 volts can also be set, but reduced output currents are available at these higher voltages. In fact a maximum output current of less than one amp is available with an output voltage of 24 volts. The output noise level can also be quite high at these voltages when heavy currents are drawn. However, it is still useful to be able to set these higher output voltages which are fully usable when only low output currents are required.

Some form of over-current protection is essential for a bench power supply, as overloads are likely to occur quite frequently. This circuit is protected against output short circuits and other overloads by an output current limiting circuit. This normally operates at a current of about 1.4 amps, but it can be set to a lower level of about 100 milliamps if preferred. This lower limit is useful when testing delicate circuits that could be 'zapped' by high currents.

System Operation

Figure 1.1 shows the block diagram for the pushbutton power supply unit. The PIC processor performs only a relatively minor role in this circuit, and it really just functions as a form of up/down counter and clock circuit. It starts at zero and then counts up and down under the control of the pushbutton switches. Its eight-bit output is fed to an analogue to digital converter, and this provides an output voltage in the range zero to 2.55 volts. In other words, an output potential of 10 millivolts per least significant bit. The PIC processor and the analogue to digital converter both require a well-stabilised five-volt supply, and this is derived from the main 30-volt supply via a simple series regulator circuit.

The output voltage range from the analogue to digital converter is inadequate and must be boosted by an amplifier. This amplifier has a voltage gain of 10, giving an output voltage range of zero to 25.5 volts in one hundred-millivolt increments. On the face of it, this should give a maximum output to voltage of 25.5 volts, but the maximum count from the up/down counter is limited to 240. The maximum output potential from the circuit is therefore 24 volts. Obviously this circuit could provide potentials up to the full 25.5-volt limit, but at voltages above 24 volts the performance of the unit becomes too low to be worthwhile.

As the amplifier can only provide a maximum output current of a few milliamps a buffer amplifier is needed to provide the high output currents of over one amp required in this application. The current limiting circuit detects excessive output currents and when necessary pulls the output of the buffer amplifier lower in voltage. This limits the maximum output current to 1.4 amps (or 200 milliamps) even with a short

2

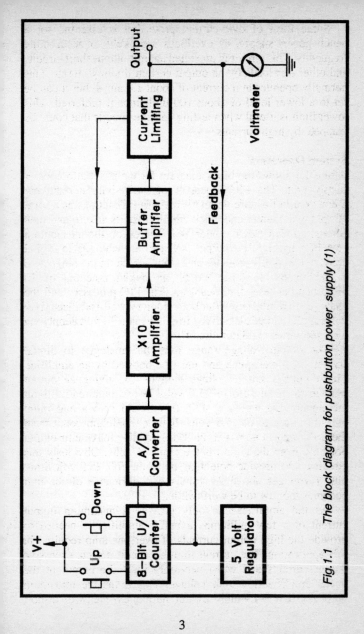

Fig. 1.1   The block diagram for pushbutton power supply (1)

circuit across the output. The negative feedback for the voltage amplifier stage is obtained from the output of the circuit so that it compensates for any voltage losses through the buffer amplifier and current limiting stages. A simple analogue voltmeter monitors the output voltage and enables it to be set with reasonable accuracy. A digital multimeter should be used to monitor the output of the unit if the output potential must be set with a high degree of accuracy.

Circuit Operation

The circuit diagram for the PIC processor and digital to analogue converter stages appears in Figure 1.2. IC1 is the PIC processor and this is used with its internal clock in the C-R mode. The discrete timing components are resistor R1 and capacitor C1. These set the clock frequency at around 25kHz to 30kHz, but as a C-R clock is used its frequency can not be set with great precision. In this application the exact clock frequency is of no great consequence, and a C-R clock circuit is perfectly adequate. Port A of IC1 is used as a nibble input that reads the four pushbutton switches (S1 to S4). Resistors R2 to R5 normally hold these inputs low, but operating a pushbutton switch pulls the appropriate input high. The software within the PIC processor detects this and it then provides the appropriate action.

Port B is used as an eight-bit output port, which drives the analogue to digital converter (IC2). There is a minor problem in that the outputs of the PIC processor default to inputs at switch on, and only become outputs once the software initialisation has been completed. This results in a brief output pulse at maximum potential each time the unit is switched on. This problem is overcome by using pull-down resistors on the outputs of IC1 so that these lines are held low until they have been set up as an output port. Resistors R6 to R13 provide the pull-down function. IC2 requires only two discrete components and these are needed by its built-in 2.55-volt reference source. This is a simple shunt regulator circuit, which has R14 as its load resistor and C2 to provide decoupling. It is possible to use an external voltage reference source, but the built-in circuit offers a very high level of performance and there is no point in using an external regulator circuit.

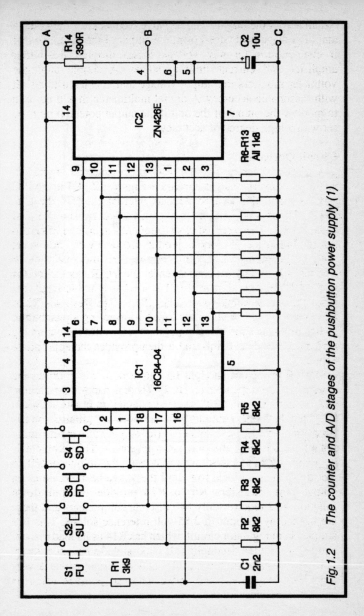

Fig.1.2   The counter and A/D stages of the pushbutton power supply (1)

5

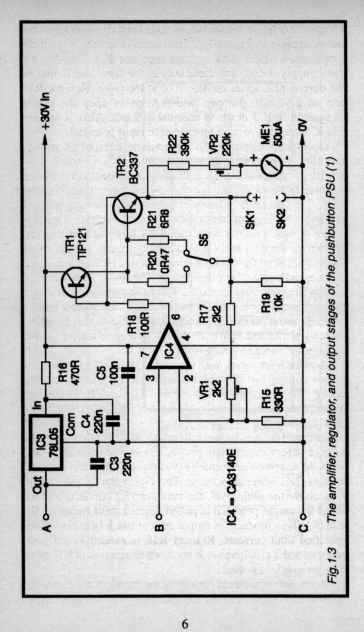

Fig. 1.3 The amplifier, regulator, and output stages of the pushbutton PSU (1)

IC4 = CA3140E

The circuit diagram for the output stages and five-volt regulator circuit appears in Figure 1.3. The regulator circuit is a simple type based on monolithic voltage regulator IC3. This has the usual supply decoupling capacitors at the input and output of the device, plus series resistor R16 at the input. Resistor R16 acts as a voltage dropper, which helps to keep the power dissipation in IC3 down to acceptable levels. Also, it ensures that IC3 does not receive an excessive input potential.

Operational amplifier IC4 is used as the basis of the voltage amplifier stage, and this is basically just a standard non-inverting mode circuit. Its voltage gain is controlled by the negative feedback circuit, which includes preset potentiometer VR1. This preset is adjusted to produce a voltage gain of precisely 10 so that the required output voltage range is obtained. Note that the device used for IC4 is a type that can operate in single supply DC amplifier circuits. Most other operational amplifiers cannot operate in this type of circuit and will not work properly in this design. The buffer amplifier is an emitter follower stage based on TR1. This device is actually a Darlington type, and it offers an extremely high current gain of typically about 5000. It is therefore well able to supply output currents of over one amp even though it receives a drive current of no more than a few milliamps from IC4.

A resistor in series with the output is used to detect the output current that flows, and activates the current limiting circuit. Two resistors are available (R20 and R21) and the required resistor is selected using switch S5. These respectively provide maximum output currents of 1.4 amps and 100 milliamps. The current limiting circuit has no effect until the voltage across the current sensing resistor reaches about 0.7 volts. At this point transistor TR2 starts to turn on and pulls the base of TR1 lower in voltage. The higher the output current rises above the limit level, the stronger TR2 conducts and the lower the output potential is pulled. Even a short circuit on the output fails to produce an output current much in excess of the specified limit currents. Resistor R18 is needed to aid good stability and it also helps to keep down dissipation in IC4 when a major overload occurs.

A simple voltmeter is formed at the output of the circuit by resistor R22, preset resistor VR2, and moving coil panel meter

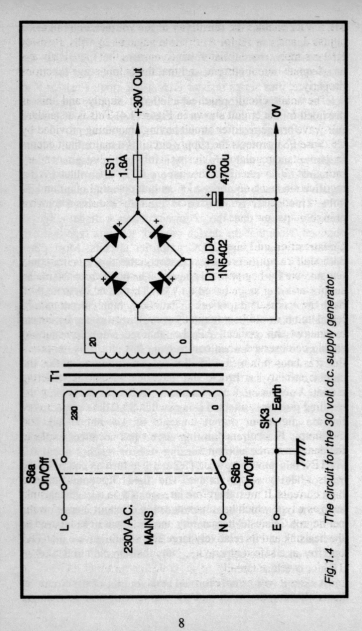

Fig. 1.4   The circuit for the 30 volt d.c. supply generator

8

ME1. VR2 enables the sensitivity of the voltmeter circuit to be adjusted, and it is set for a full-scale value of 25 volts. Resistor R19 is simply a load resistor, which ensures that there is always an adequate output current, and that the output stage functions properly.

The main circuit requires a 30-volt supply and this is provided by the circuit shown in Figure 1.4. This is a standard full-wave bridge rectifier circuit having smoothing provided by C6. Fuse FS1 protects the supply circuit if a major fault occurs in the voltage regulator. Mains transformer T1 has a secondary rating of 20 volts, but this is an RMS AC value. After rectification and smoothing a DC output potential of around 30 volts is produced with zero loading, but this reduces somewhat at high output currents.

Construction and Use

Although this circuit is not particularly complex it is definitely not suitable for beginners. The unit is powered from the mains supply, and it must therefore only be constructed by those who have the necessary experience. The mains supply is potentially lethal and it would be potentially very dangerous for beginners to attempt this project. All the standard safety precautions should be observed when constructing this unit. It is important that it is housed in a case of all metal construction and that the case is reliably earthed to the mains earth lead. A soldertag mounted on one of the mounting bolts for T1 makes a good earthing point for the case. It is essential that the case is a type that has a lid or outer cover secured by screws, and not a lid that can simply be unclipped, as this would provide easy access to the dangerous mains wiring.

TR1 is a power transistor and it has to dissipate over 30 watts when the supply is used with low output voltages and high currents. It must therefore be mounted on a large heatsink, such as a type which has a power rating of about 2 or 2.5 watts per degree Celsius. Alternatively, the metal case can be used as the heatsink and its relatively large size should ensure that TR1 operates at a safe temperature. Note that the metal heat-tab of TR1 connects internally to its collector terminal and that in most cases it will be necessary to insulate TR1 from the case or heatsink using the usual mica or plastic washer and insulating bush. Make quite sure that the insulation is effective, preferably using a continuity tester, as a flaw in the insulation is likely to cause a short circuit across the unregulated 30-volt supply. The fuse should 'blow' and prevent any damage to the components, but it is obviously preferable not to put this to the 'acid test'.

These days it seems to be normal for mains transformers to have twin secondary windings, but in this case a single 20-volt winding is all that is needed. Most mains transformers which have twin secondary windings have the option of using them in either series of parallel, and in this case it is probably two 20-volt windings connected in parallel that will have to be used. Two secondaries rated at 10 volts and 2.5 amps are also suitable, but it is unlikely that a suitable transformer could be obtained. Note that it is only acceptable to connect twin secondary windings in parallel if the transformer is specifically designed for that method of connection. Using parallel connection with a component that is not designed for that method of wiring is likely to cause a very high secondary current to flow and could burn out the windings. Check the manufacturer's or retailer's literature to ensure that the transformer you use is suitable for this method of connection.

As this project connects to the mains supply and also handles relatively high voltages and currents, it is essential to thoroughly check all the wiring before switching on and testing it. Start with both preset resistors at roughly the middle settings. Initially meter ME1 should register zero, but by operating the two 'up' pushbutton switches it should be possible to increase the output voltage. It should then be possible to decrease it again using the two 'down' pushbutton switches. The 'fast' switches are used to get the output voltage to approximately the required level, and the 'slow' switches are then used to adjust the output potential more precisely.

Before the unit can be used in earnest the two preset resistors must be set up correctly. First set the output voltage at maximum, and using a multimeter to monitor the output potential adjust VR1 for a reading of precisely 24 volts. Then adjust VR2 so that a reading of exactly 24 volts is produced on panel meter ME1. The unit is then ready for use. The meter can be recalibrated if required, and with most meters the front simply unclips. By undoing a couple of small screws the scale plate can then be removed and recalibrated using rub-on transfers. While this process is not difficult, great care has to be exercised because meter movements are very delicate and easily damaged. Also, readings on the existing scale are easily converted into corresponding output voltages as it is just a matter of dividing by two.

Software

The initial part of the program sets up port B as an eight-bit output port, and sets the value of the COUNT register at zero. The value output to the digital to analogue converter is held in COUNT, and the output voltage is therefore set at its required initial value of zero. The main program loop reads the four pushbutton switches and places the result in BUTTONS. It then checks each bit of the lower nibble and calls up the appropriate subroutine if a button has been pressed. The subroutines that provide the fast and slow upwards changes in voltage (FUP and SUP) are basically the same, but a longer delay loop is used in SUP so that it increments the output voltage more slowly. In both cases the routine starts by loading the value in COUNT into the W register, and it is then bitwise XORed with a value of F0 (240 in decimal). This is the highest value that the counter must contain, as it is the value that gives an output potential of 24 volts. If the count is at F0, the value in the W register will be zero after the XOR operation, and the zero flag will be set. This is detected by the next part of the routine, which then returns the program to the main loop. If the count is less than F0, it is incremented by one, and then written to both port B and the COUNT register. After a short or long delay, depending on whether FUP or SUP is being performed, the routine terminates and the program returns to the main loop.

The subroutines that decrement the count (FDOWN and SDOWN) operate in a similar fashion, but initially the value in the counter is checked to determine whether or not it has reached zero. If it is at zero, the routine is terminated and the program returns to the main loop. This ensures that the value in the counter does not cycle through zero, which would take it to a value of FF (255 decimal). Allowing the count to cycle through zero to a value of 255 would provide a quick means of going from a very low voltage to a very high one.

11

Unfortunately, it would also make it easy to inadvertently set a high output voltage when trying to set a very low output potential. It is safer to include a block to prevent the count cycling through zero. If the count is more than zero, it is decremented by one and then written to COUNT and to port B. After an appropriate delay the program then returns to the main loop again.

```
;**************************************************
;
;Pushbutton PSU 1 Program
;**************************************************
;
;
STATUS    EQU       03
Z         EQU       02
BDIR      EQU       06
PORTA     EQU       05
PORTB     EQU       06
BUTTONS   EQU       0C
COUNT     EQU       0D
DEL       EQU       0F
          BSF       STATUS,5    ;Select page 1
          CLRW
          MOVWF     BDIR        ;Sets Port B as outputs
          BCF       STATUS,5    ;Select page 0
          CLRF      PORTB       ;Sets Port B to zero
          CLRF      COUNT       ;Sets count at zero
MAIN      MOVF      PORTA,0     ;Read Port A
          MOVWF     BUTTONS     ;Store result
          BTFSC     BUTTONS,0
          CALL      FUP
          BTFSC     BUTTONS,1
          CALL      SUP
          BTFSC     BUTTONS,2
          CALL      FDOWN
          BTFSC     BUTTONS,3
          CALL      SDOWN
          GOTO      MAIN
FUP       MOVF      COUNT,0
          BCF       STATUS,Z
          XORLW     0xF0        ;Limits count to 240 decimal
```

12

```
          BTFSC     STATUS,Z
          RETURN
          INCF      COUNT,1
          MOVF      COUNT,0
          MOVWF     PORTB
          MOVLW     0xA0
          MOVWF     DEL
DLOOP     NOP
          DECFSZ    DEL,1
          GOTO      DLOOP
          RETURN
SUP       MOVF      COUNT,0
          BCF       STATUS,Z
          XORLW     0xF0       ;Limits count to 240 decimal
          BTFSC     STATUS,Z
          RETURN
          INCF      COUNT,1
          MOVF      COUNT,0
          MOVWF     PORTB
          MOVLW     0xFF
          MOVWF     DEL
DLOOP2    NOP
          NOP
          NOP
          NOP
          NOP
          NOP
          NOP
          NOP
          DECFSZ    DEL,1
          GOTO      DLOOP2
          RETURN
FDOWN     BCF       STATUS,Z
          MOVF      COUNT,0
          BTFSC     STATUS,Z   ;Prevents count cycling through
                               zero
          RETURN
          DECF      COUNT,1
          MOVF      COUNT,0
          MOVWF     PORTB
```

13

```
              MOVLW    0xA0
              MOVWF    DEL
DLOOP3        NOP
              DECFSZ   DEL,1
              GOTO     DLOOP3
              RETURN
SDOWN         BCF      STATUS,Z
              MOVF     COUNT,0
              BTFSC    STATUS,Z    ;Prevents count cycling through
                                   zero
              RETURN
              DECF     COUNT,1
              MOVF     COUNT,0
              MOVWF    PORTB
              MOVLW    0xFF
              MOVWF    DEL
DLOOP4        NOP
              NOP
              NOP
              NOP
              NOP
              NOP
              NOP
              NOP
              DECFSZ   DEL,1
              GOTO     DLOOP4
              RETURN
END
```

Components for Pushbutton Power Supply (1) (Figures 1.2, 1.3 and 1.4)

Resistors (0.25 watt 5% carbon film unless noted)

R1	3k9
R2, R3, R4, R5	8k2 (4 off)
R6 to R13	1k8 (8 off)
R14	390R
R15	330R
R16	470R

14

R17	2k2
R18	100R 1 watt
R19	10k
R20	0R47 2 watt
R21	6R8
R22	390k

Potentiometers
| VR1 | 2k2 min hor preset |
| VR2 | 220k min hor preset |

Capacitors
C1	2n2 polyester
C2	10μ 25V elect
C3, C4	220n ceramic (2 off)
C5	100n ceramic
C6	4700μ 35V elect

Semiconductors
IC1	PIC 16C84-04
IC2	ZN426E
IC3	78L05 (+5V 100mA regulator)
IC4	CA3140E
TR1	TIP121
TR2	BC337
D1, D2, D3, D4	1N5402 (4 off)

Miscellaneous
S1, S2, S3, S4	Push-to-make pushbutton switches (4 off)
S5	s.p.d.t. min toggle switch
S6	Rotary mains switch
ME1	50μA moving coil panel meter
SK1	Red 4mm socket
SK2	Black 4mm socket
SK3	Green 4mm socket
FS1	20mm 'quickblow' 1.6A fuse
T1	Standard mains primary, 20 volt secondary rated at 2.5A or more

8-pin DIL holder, 14-pin DIL holder, 18-pin DIL holder, circuit board, metal case with screw fitting lid or cover, control knob, heatsink and TO220 insulation kit for TR1 (see text), wire, solder, etc.

Pushbutton Power Supply (2)

This bench power supply circuit has a specification that is essentially the same as that of the previous design. However, its method of control is rather different, although it still uses pushbutton switches. Like the previous design it starts with a zero output voltage, and the output of voltage can then be set at one of eight preset levels using a bank of eight pushbutton switches. The available output voltages using the suggested software are 3, 5, 6, 9, 12, 15, 18, and 20 volts. By substituting the appropriate values into the program it is possible to have any desired output voltages from 0 to 24 volts in 0.1 volt increments. The output voltage can be changed at any time by simply pressing the appropriate pushbutton switch.

Circuit Operation

The circuit diagram for the counter and analogue to digital converter stages of the Mark 2 pushbutton power supply unit appears in Figure 1.5. This design is based on a PIC 16C55-RC/P processor rather than a 16C84, since eight input lines are needed in order to read the pushbutton switches. With eight of its input/output lines used to drive the converter, the 16C84 has only four lines left to act as inputs. These could probably read eight switches using scanning techniques, but it is easier to simply base the design on a 16C55. This has two eight-bit input/output ports plus a four-bit type. Port B is used to drive the converter, port C reads the eight pushbutton switches, and the four lines of port A are left unused. Apart from this the circuit is essentially the same as the equivalent section of the original design.

Figure 1.6 shows the circuit diagram for the amplifier, five-volt regulator, and output stages of the unit. The circuit for the raw 30-volt supply generator appears in Figure 1.7. In both cases the circuits are identical to the equivalent sections of the Mark 1 design except that some changes in the component numbering have been made necessary by the changes to the counter circuit.

Software

The first part of the program sets port C as eight output lines, and then the program enters the main loop. This repeatedly tests

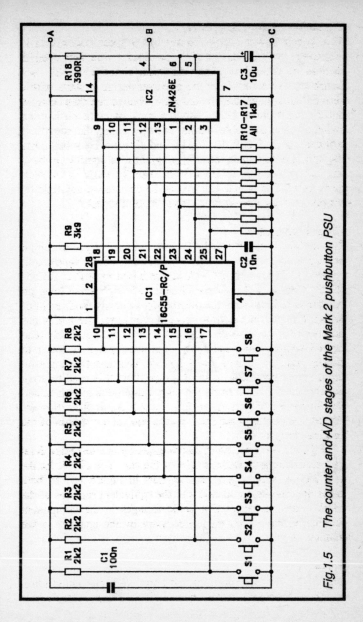

Fig.1.5 The counter and A/D stages of the Mark 2 pushbutton PSU

17

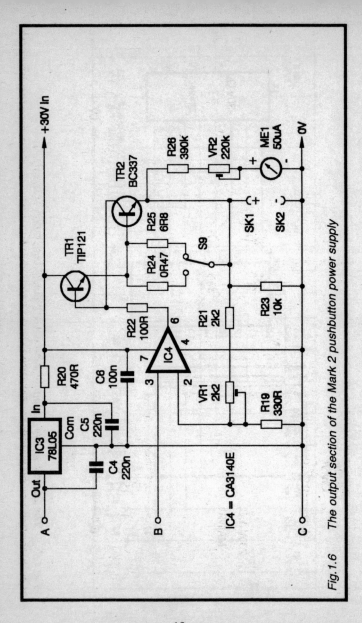

Fig.1.6   The output section of the Mark 2 pushbutton power supply

18

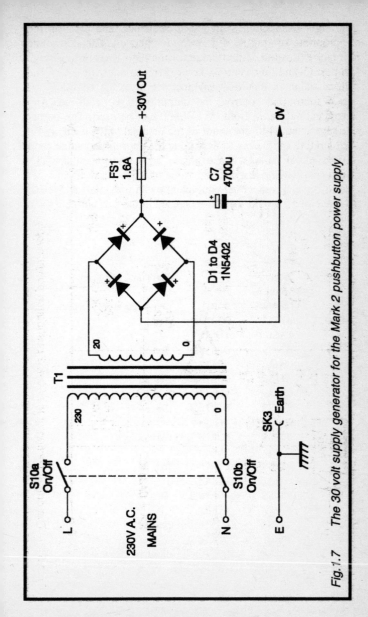

Fig. 1.7   The 30 volt supply generator for the Mark 2 pushbutton power supply

19

the eight pushbutton switches, in sequence, and calls up the appropriate subroutine if a switch is operated. The subroutine simply writes the correct value for the required output voltage to port C, and then returns the program to the main loop. The literal value in the MOVLW instruction at the beginning of each subroutine controls the output voltage produced. Any hexadecimal value from 00 to 0xF0 can be used. The output voltage is equal to one-tenth of the decimal value used, and it is therefore quite easy to determine the appropriate value for a given output voltage. For example, an output potential of 8.5 volts would require a decimal value of 8.5×10, or 85 in other words. The hexadecimal equivalent of 85 (decimal) is 55, and a value of 55 would therefore be used in the subroutine.

```
PORTB    EQU      06
PORTC    EQU      07
         CLRW
         TRIS     07           ;Sets Port C as outputs
         MOVLW    3F
         MOVWF    PORTC        ;Sets output at 0V initially
LOOP     BTFSS    PORTB,0      ;Test S1
         CALL     VOLT1
         BTFSS    PORTB,1      ;Test S2
         CALL     VOLT2
         BTFSS    PORTB,2      ;Test S3
         CALL     VOLT3
         BTFSS    PORTB,3      ;Test S4
         CALL     VOLT4
         BTFSS    PORTB,4      ;Test S5
         CALL     VOLT5
         BTFSS    PORTB,5      ;Test S6
         CALL     VOLT6
         BTFSS    PORTB,6      ;Test S7
         CALL     VOLT7
         BTFSS    PORTB,7      ;Test S8
         CALL     VOLT8
         GOTO     LOOP         ;Read switches indefinitely
VOLT1    MOVLW    1E
         MOVWF    PORTC        ;Set output at 3 volts
         RETLW    00
```

```
VOLT2    MOVLW    50
         MOVWF    PORTC    ;Set output at 5 volts
         RETLW    00
VOLT3    MOVLW    3C
         MOVWF    PORTC    ;Set output at 6 volts
         RETLW    00
VOLT4    MOVLW    5A
         MOVWF    PORTC    ;Set output at 9 volts
         RETLW    00
VOLT5    MOVLW    78
         MOVWF    PORTC    ;Set output at 12 volts
         RETLW    00
VOLT6    MOVLW    96
         MOVWF    PORTC    ;Set output at 15 volts
         RETLW    00
VOLT7    MOVLW    0xB4
         MOVWF    PORTC    ;Set output at 18 volts
         RETLW    00
VOLT8    MOVLW    0xC8
         MOVWF    PORTC    ;Set output at 20 volts
         RELW     00
         END
```

Components for Pushbutton Power Supply (2) (Figures 1.5, 1.6 and 1.7)

Resistors (0.25 watt 5% carbon film unless noted)

R1 to R8, R21	2k2 (9 off)
R9	3k9
R10 to R17	1k8 (8 off)
R18	390R
R19	330R
R20	470R
R22	100R 1 watt
R23	10k
R24	0R47 2 watt
R25	6R8
R26	390k

Potentiometers

VR1	2k2 min hor preset
VR2	220k min hor preset

Capacitors

C1	100n ceramic
C2	10n polyester
C3	10µ 25V elect
C4, C5	220n ceramic (2 off)
C6	100n ceramic
C7	4700µ 35V elect

Semiconductors

IC1	PIC 16C55-RC/P
IC2	ZN426E
IC3	78L05 (+5V 100mA regulator)
IC4	CA3140E
TR1	TIP121
TR2	BC337
D1, D2, D3, D4	1N5402 (4 off)

Miscellaneous

S1 to S8	Push-to-make pushbutton switches (8 off)
S9	s.p.d.t. min toggle switch
S10	Rotary mains switch
ME1	50µA moving coil panel meter
SK1	Red 4mm socket
SK2	Black 4mm socket
SK3	Green 4mm socket
FS1	20mm 'quickblow' 1.6A fuse
T1	Standard mains primary, 20 volt secondary rated at 2.5A or more

8-pin DIL holder, 14-pin DIL holder, 18-pin DIL holder, metal case with screw fitting lid or cover, control knob, heatsink and TO220 insulation kit for TR1 (see text), wire, solder, etc.

Voltage Probe

This project could be regarded as the analogue equivalent of a logic probe. It has a LED bargraph display with the LEDs operating at threshold potentials of 0.5, 1, 2, 5, 10, 15, 25, and

50 volts. The input voltage can not be measured with the same degree of accuracy that is available using an analogue or digital multimeter, but the approximate input voltage can be quickly gauged. The input resistance of the circuit is quite high at about 1.1 megohms, and the unit therefore places minimal loading on the circuit under test.

The circuit demonstrates the use of the PIC 16C71 as a bargraph display driver, and in this example it drives an eight LED display. There are, of course, several chips that are designed specifically for use as bargraph drivers. Devices for both linear and logarithmic scaling are available, but even so, the bargraph chips do not always provide the threshold levels that your applications require. It is not too difficult to produce custom bargraph circuits based on operational amplifiers and resistors that have any desired threshold voltages. This is a rather cumbersome way of doing things though, and the PIC 16C71 offers a neater solution to the problem. The eight-bit resolution of its analogue to digital converter gives a wide dynamic range, and the threshold levels can, to a large extent, be selected in software rather than by the hardware.

Figure 1.8 shows the circuit diagram for the voltage probe project. R1, R2, and VR1 form an attenuator at the channel 0 input of the processor, and this reduces the sensitivity of the circuit by a factor of about ten or so. The 5-volt full-scale value of the converter therefore becomes a full-scale input potential of over 50 volts at the input of the probe. VR1 is adjusted to give the circuit precisely the required input sensitivity. D1 is a zener protection diode that limits the maximum input voltage to the PIC processor to about 5.6 volts. With an input of the wrong polarity it limits the input potential to IC1 at about −0.7 volts. This prevents any damage if the probe is connected to a grossly excessive input voltage, or if it is connected with the wrong polarity. It is still advisable to only use the unit in circuits that carry a maximum potential of about 100 volts or less.

R11 and C2 are the timing components for the C-R clock circuit. The exact clock frequency is unimportant in this application, but it must be quite high if the LED display is to be flicker-free. The eight LEDs are driven from port B via current limiting resistors R3 to R10. In order to keep the total current consumption of the circuit within reasonable bounds (and the

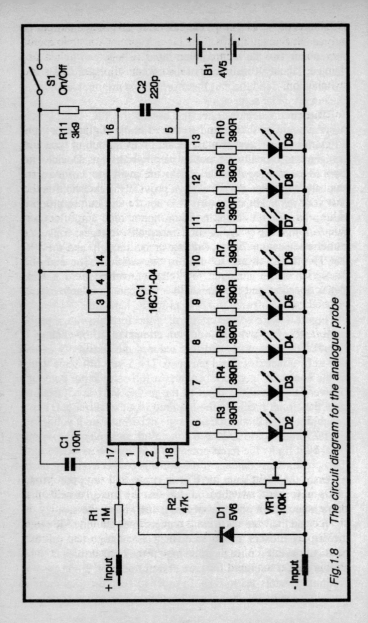

Fig. 1.8   The circuit diagram for the analogue probe

safe limits of the PIC chip) the LEDs are driven at a current of only about five milliamps. This gives a current consumption of only about two milliamps when no LEDs are switched on, rising to about 40 milliamps or so when all eight LEDs are switched on.

Software

A fair amount of setting up is required at the beginning of this program because port B must be set up as an output type and port A has to be set to the mode where RA0 acts as an analogue input. The program then goes into the main loop which first reads the converter and then runs a series of eight checks on the returned value. The basic idea is to add certain numbers to the value read from the converter, checking the carry flag after each calculation. If the carry flag is set, the value from the converter was above a certain figure, and the appropriate LED is switched on. This table shows the converter value for each of the threshold voltages, together with the number used in the ADLW instruction that tests to see if that threshold value has been reached.

Voltage	Conv. Value (Dec.)	Value Added (Dec/Hex)
0.5	2	254/FE
1	4	252/FC
2	8	248/F8
5	20	236/EC
10	40	216/D8
15	60	196/C4
25	100	156/9C
50	200	56/38

Once the eight tests have been made and the appropriate LEDs have been switched on, the display must he held in a stable state for a short period of time. Then the display is cleared and the whole process is repeated indefinitely. Although the display flickers, provided it flickers at a high rate it looks perfectly stable. A high clock frequency ensures that any strobing is far too rapid for it to be noticeable.

```
;**************************************************
;Voltage Probe Program
;**************************************************
;
CARRY     EQU       00
STATUS    EQU       03
BDIR      EQU       06
ADCON     EQU       08
PORTB     EQU       06
ADRES     EQU       09
STORE     EQU       0C
CNTR      EQU       0D
          BSF       STATUS,5      ;Select page 1
          CLRW
          MOVWF     BDIR          ;Sets Port B as outputs
          CLRF      ADCON         ;Sets RA0–3 as A/D inputs
          BCF       STATUS, 5     ;Select page 0
          MOVLW     0xC1
          MOVWF     ADCON         ;Select Ch0/Int clock
LOOP      BSF       ADCON,2       ;Start conversion
          NOP                     ;Wait
          MOVF      ADRES,0       ;Place conversion in W
          MOVWF     STORE         ;Place conversion in STORE
          BCF       STATUS,CARRY
          ADDLW     0xFE          ;Check for reading over 0.5V
          BTFSC     STATUS,CARRY
          BSF       PORTB,0
          MOVF      STORE,0       ;Place conversion in W
          BCF       STATUS,CARRY
          ADDLW     0xFC          ;Check for reading over 1V
          BTFSC     STATUS,CARRY
          BSF       PORTB,1
          MOVF      STORE,0       ;Place conversion in W
          BCF       STATUS,CARRY
          ADDLW     0xF8          ;Check for reading over 2V
          BTFSC     STATUS,CARRY
          BSF       PORTB,2
          MOVF      STORE,0       ;Place conversion in W
          BCF       STATUS,CARRY
          ADDLW     0xEC          ;Check for reading over 5V
```

```
        BTFSC      STATUS,CARRY
        BSF        PORTB,3
        MOVF       STORE,0    ;Place conversion in W
        BCF        STATUS,CARRY
        ADDLW      0xD8       ;Check for reading over 10V
        BTFSC      STATUS,CARRY
        BSF        PORTB,4
        MOVF       STORE,0    ;Place conversion in W
        BCF        STATUS,CARRY
        ADDLW      0xC4       ;Check for reading over 15V
        BTFSC      STATUS,CARRY
        BSF        PORTB,5
        MOVF       STORE,0    ;Place conversion in W
        BCF        STATUS,CARRY
        ADDLW      0x9C       ;Check for reading over 25V
        BTFSC      STATUS,CARRY
        BSF        PORTB,6
        MOVF       STORE,0    ;Place conversion in W
        BCF        STATUS,CARRY
        ADDLW      0x38       ;Check for reading over 50V
        BTFSC      STATUS,CARRY
        BSF        PORTB,7
        MOVLW      0xFF
        MOVWF      CNTR
DELAY   DECFSZ     CNTR,1     ;Delay before repeating procedure
        GOTO       DELAY
        CLRF       PORTB      ;Clear display
        GOTO       LOOP
        END
```

Components for Analogue Voltage Probe (Figure 1.8)

Resistors (all 0.25 watt 5% carbon film)
R1   1M
R2   47k
R3 to R10   390R (8 off)
R11   3k9

Potentiometer
VR1   100k min hor preset

Capacitors
C1   100n ceramic
C2   220p ceramic plate or polystyrene

Semiconductors
IC1   PIC 16C71-04
D1   BZY88C5V6 or similar 5.6 volt 400mV
                        zener diode
D2 to D9   Red panel LEDs (8 off)

Miscellaneous
S1   s.p.s.t. min toggle switch
B1   4.5 volt (3 × AA or AAA size cells in holder)
Case, circuit board, 18-pin DIL holder, battery connector, wire,
solder, etc.

Dot Mode Voltage Probe

This project is essentially the same as the previous one, but it
uses a so-called 'dot' mode display rather than a true bargraph.
In other words, if the input potential is (say) 12 volts, only D6
(the LED which indicates the 10 volt threshold level) will
switch on. With a 'proper' bargraph D2 to D6 would all switch
on. In terms of display clarity a true bargraph is almost
certainly better than a dot type, but it has the major drawback
of a relatively high current consumption. In order to keep the
current drain down to acceptable levels it is normal for the
LEDs in a true bargraph to be run at quite low currents. By
using dot mode operation it is possible to use a higher LED
current and still have greatly reduced current consumption.

The circuit diagram for the dot mode voltage probe is
shown in Figure 1.9, and it is basically the same as the one for
the true bargraph version. The only difference is that the current
limiting resistors for the LEDs (R3 to R10) have been reduced
in value. This increases the LED current to around 10
milliamps. The current consumption of the circuit is about one
to two milliamps under standby conditions, rising to around 11
milliamps when the display is active.

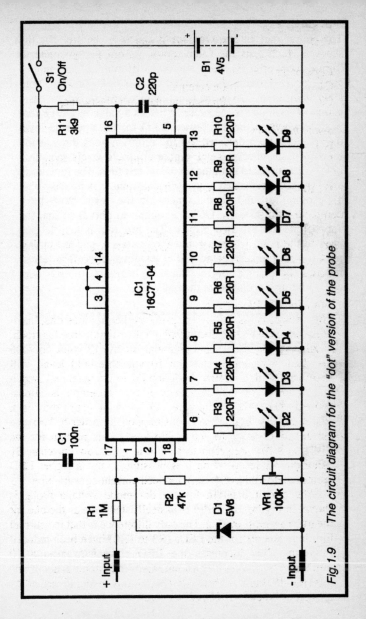

Fig. 1.9   The circuit diagram for the "dot" version of the probe

Software

The initial part of the program is much as before, but the section which tests the value returned from the analogue to digital converter is substantially different. This time a subroutine is called if the returned value is above the threshold level. A different subroutine is called by each test, but the basic action of each one is the same. It places a value in DOTS that would switch on the appropriate LED for the threshold level that has just been detected. As the program goes through the series of tests, checking ever-higher threshold levels, the value in DOTS is updated until the threshold test fails. The remaining tests are still performed anyway because there is no easy way of looping around them. Once all the tests have been completed, the value in DOTS is output to port B so that the appropriate LED is switched on. The program is then looped back to the point where a conversion is taken, and the testing process is then repeated. The program therefore loops indefinitely, taking a new reading at the beginning of each loop, and updating the display at the end.

```
;**************************************************
;Dot Mode Voltage Probe Program
;**************************************************
;
CARRY     EQU      00
DOTS      EQU      0E
STATUS    EQU      03
BDIR      EQU      06
ADCON     EQU      08
PORTB     EQU      06
ADRES     EQU      09
STORE     EQU      0C
CNTR      EQU      0D
          BSF      STATUS,5    ;Select page 1
          CLRW
          MOVWF    BDIR        ;Sets Port B as outputs
          CLRF     ADCON       ;Sets RA0–3 as A/D inputs
          BCF      STATUS,5    ;Select page 0
          MOVLW    0xC1
          MOVWF    ADCON       ;Selection Ch0/Int clock
```

30

```
LOOP      BSF       ADCON,2         ;Start conversion
          NOP                       ;Wait
          MOVF      ADRES,0         ;Place conversion in W
          MOVWF     STORE           ;Place conversion in STORE
          BCF       STATUS,CARRY
          ADDLW     0xFE            ;Check for reading over 0.5V
          BTFSC     STATUS,CARRY
          CALL      DOT1
          MOVF      STORE,0         ;Place conversion in W
          BCF       STATUS,CARRY
          ADDLW     0xFC            ;Check for reading over 1V
          BTFSC     STATUS,CARRY
          CALL      DOT2
          MOVF      STORE,0         ;Place conversion in W
          BCF       STATUS,CARRY
          ADDLW     0xF8            ;Check for reading over 2V
          BTFSC     STATUS,CARRY
          CALL      DOT3
          MOVF      STORE,0         ;Place conversion in W
          BCF       STATUS,CARRY
          ADDLW     0xEC            ;Check for reading over 5V
          BTFSC     STATUS,CARRY
          CALL      DOT4
          MOVF      STORE,0         ;Place conversion in W
          BCF       STATUS,CARRY
          ADDLW     0xD8            ;Check for reading over 10V
          BTFSC     STATUS,CARRY
          CALL      DOT5
          MOVF      STORE,0         ;Place conversion in W
          BCF       STATUS,CARRY
          ADDLW     0xC4            ;Check for reading over 15V
          BTFSC     STATUS,CARRY
          CALL      DOT6
          MOVF      STORE,0         ;Place conversion in W
          BCF       STATUS,CARRY
          ADDLW     0x9C            ;Check for reading over 25V
          BTFSC     STATUS,CARRY
          CALL      DOT7
          MOVF      STORE,0         ;Place conversion in W
          BCF       STATUS,CARRY
```

31

```
        ADDLW       0x38        ;Check for reading over 50V
        BTFSC       STATUS,CARRY
        CALL        DOT8
        MOVF        DOTS,0
        MOVWF       PORTB
        GOTO        LOOP
DOT1    MOVLW       01
        MOVWF       DOTS
        RETURN
DOT2    MOVLW       02
        MOVWF       DOTS
        RETURN
DOT3    MOVLW       04
        MOVWF       DOTS
        RETURN
DOT4    MOVLW       08
        MOVWF       DOTS
        RETURN
DOT5    MOVLW       10
        MOVWF       DOTS
        RETURN
DOT6    MOVLW       20
        MOVWF       DOTS
        RETURN
DOT7    MOVLW       40
        MOVWF       DOTS
        RETURN
DOT8    MOVLW       80
        MOVWF       DOTS
        RETURN
        END
```

Components for Dot Mode Voltage Probe (Figure 1.9)

Resistors (all 0.25 watt 5% carbon film)
R1   1M
R2   47k
R3 to R10   220R (8 off)
R11   3k9

Potentiometer
VR1   100k min hor preset

Capacitors
C1   100n ceramic
C2   220p ceramic plate or polystyrene

Semiconductors
IC1   PIC 16C71-04
D1   BZY88C5V6 or similar 5.6 volt 400mW
                       zener diode
D2 to D9   Red panel LEDs (8 off)

Miscellaneous
S1   s.p.s.t. min toggle switch
B1   4.5 volt (3 x AA or AAA size cells in holder)
Case, circuit board, 18-pin DIL holder, battery connector, wire,
solder, etc.

Transistor Tester – 1
This simple transistor checker uses a PIC 16C71 to drive a ten
LED bargraph that covers these current gain ranges.

LED	Gain Range
None	< 20
D1	20 – 40
D2	40 – 60
D3	60 – 100
D4	100 – 200
D5	200 – 300
D6	300 – 400
D7	400 – 500
D8	500 – 600
D9	600 – 800
D10	> 800

Using a bargraph display does not provide the same degree of
resolution as either a conventional multi-digit display or a
moving coil panel meter, but it enables the current gains of test

devices to be gauged with reasonable accuracy. In common with most simple transistor checkers the current gain is not measured at a fixed collector current. With a current gain of 800 a collector current of 10 milliamps flows, and lower gains produce proportionately lower collector currents. The practical importance of this is that the current gain of a transistor tends to fall away somewhat at low collector currents. The tester may therefore give rather pessimistic readings when testing low gain components that produce relatively small collector currents. This factor obviously has to be taken into account when testing low gain transistors, but in other respects the unit is very simple and straightforward to use.

System Operation

Because PNP and NPN transistors operate with opposite supply polarities it is necessary to use a slightly different test set-up for each type. The block diagram of Figure 1.10 shows the methods used for PNP (top) and NPN testing. Testing PNP transistors is more straightforward and will be considered first. A low frequency oscillator provides a roughly squarewave signal which drives the base of the test device via current limiting resistor Ra. When the output of the oscillator is high the test device is cut off, and no significant collector current should flow into load resistor Rb. When the output of the oscillator is low, a small base current flows into the test device via Ra. This should cause a much larger current to flow in the collector circuit and the higher the gain of the transistor, the higher the collector current that will flow. The voltage developed across load resistor Rb is proportional to the current that flows through it, and this voltage is therefore proportional to the current gain of the test transistor. The values of Ra and Rb are chosen so that, together with suitable display threshold voltages, the display indicates the required gain ranges.

The arrangement used for testing NPN transistors is similar, but the test transistor receives a bias current when the output of the low frequency oscillator is high, and is cut off when the output of the oscillator is low. Due to the change of supply polarity an NPN test transistor can not directly drive the collector load resistor, but instead drives it via a current mirror. This is simply a circuit that sources a current from its output

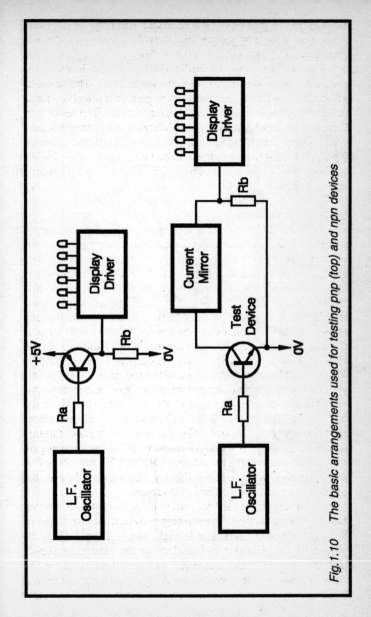

Fig. 1.10   The basic arrangements used for testing pnp (top) and npn devices

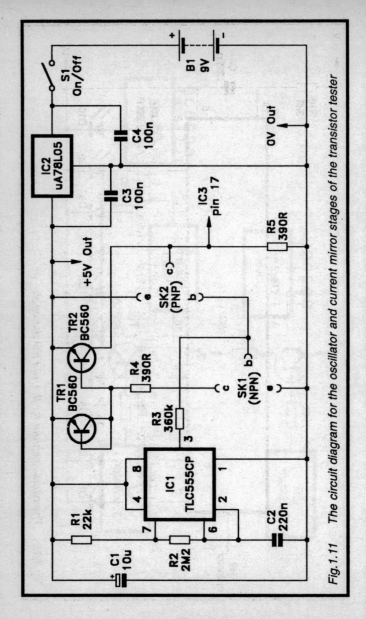

Fig.1.11   The circuit diagram for the oscillator and current mirror stages of the transistor tester

36

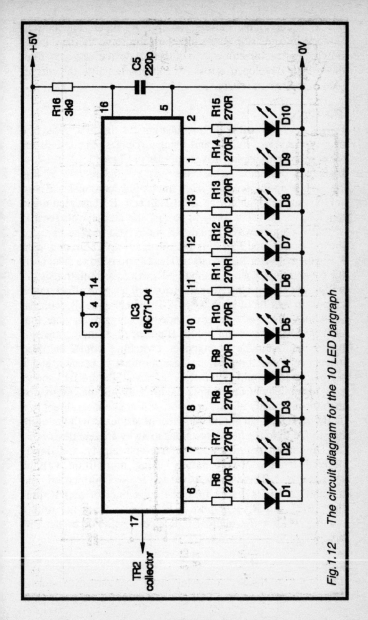

Fig. 1.12   The circuit diagram for the 10 LED bargraph

37

that is equal to the current fed into its input. The current flowing into resistor Rb is therefore the same as the current flowing in the collector circuit of the test device, and as before, the voltage developed across Rb is proportional to the current gain of the test transistor.

The Circuit

Figure 1.11 shows the circuit diagram for the low frequency oscillator, current mirror, and regulator stages. The circuit for the display and display driver appears in Figure 1.12. The low frequency oscillator is basically just a standard 555 astable circuit having R1, R2, and C2 as the timing components. These set the output frequency at about 1.5 hertz. R1 has been made much lower in value than R2 so that the output waveform is virtually a squarewave signal. R3 is the base feed resistor for the test device, and TR1 plus TR2 form a simple current mirror. R5 is the collector load resistor. There is no need to switch off the current mirror when testing PNP devices as both transistors will be cut off, and the current mirror will have no affect on the circuit. In fact there is no NPN/PNP switching at all, with the switching effectively being provided by plugging devices into the appropriate transistor holder. If preferred, a single transistor holder and suitable changeover switching could be used instead. No switching of the base terminal is needed, and a d.p.d.t. switch would therefore be sufficient. Figure 1.13 shows how to implement this simple modification. Some transistors, including virtually all power types, will not connect direct to a TO18 or TO5 transistor holder. A set of test leads will therefore be needed to make the connections to awkward test devices.

The circuit requires a stable five-volt supply, and this is derived from a 9-volt battery using monolithic voltage regulator IC2. The display driver is very straightforward, and has the ten LEDs driven from the eight lines of port B, plus lines RA2 and RA3 of port A. R16 and C5 are the timing components for the internal C-R clock oscillator of the PIC processor.

Software

The program for the transistor tester operates in a similar fashion to the programs that provide an eight-bargraph LED

38

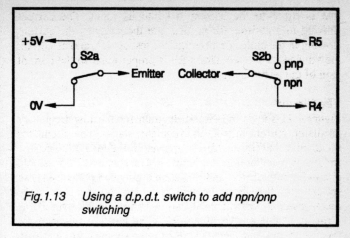

*Fig.1.13   Using a d.p.d.t. switch to add npn/pnp
            switching*

display. There is a slight difference in the setting up where lines
RA2 and RA3 must be designated as digital lines. Two
additional sections are required in the main program loop, and
when necessary these call up additional subroutines ('DOT9'
and 'DOT10'). When DOT9 is called it clears the DOTS
register (which contains the data for port A) and sets bit 2 of the
DOT2 register. DOT2 carries the data for port A, and setting bit
2 activates the ninth LED when the program returns to the main
loop. The DOT10 subroutine will also be called if the input
voltage is high enough. This routine clears bit 2 of the DOT2
register and sets bit 3. This results in the tenth LED of the
display being switched on when the program returns to the
main loop. The required 10 LED bargraph action is thus
obtained.

```
;************************************************
;Mk1 Transistor Tester Program
;************************************************
;
CARRY       EQU        00
DOTS        EQU        0E
DOTS2       EQU        0F
STATUS      EQU        03
ADIR        EQU        05
```

BDIR	EQU	06	
ADCON	EQU	08	
PORTA	EQU	05	
PORTB	EQU	06	
ADRES	EQU	09	
STORE	EQU	0C	
CNTR	EQU	0D	
	BSF	STATUS,5	;Select page 1
	MOVLW	0xF3	
	MOVWF	ADIR	;Sets RA2/3 as outputs
	CLRW		
	MOVWF	BDIR	;Sets Port B as outputs
	MOVLW	02	
	MOVWF	ADCON	;Sets RA0/1 as A/D inputs
	BCF	STATUS,5	;Select page 0
	MOVLW	0xC1	
	MOVWF	ADCON	;Select Ch0/Int clock
LOOP	BSF	ADCON,2	;Start conversion
	NOP		;Wait
	MOVF	ADRES,0	;Place conversion in W
	MOVWF	STORE	;Place conversion in STORE
	BCF	STATUS,CARRY	
	ADDLW	0xF8	;Check for gain over 20
	BTFSC	STATUS,CARRY	
	CALL	DOT1	
	MOVF	STORE,0	;Place conversion in W
	BCF	STATUS CARRY	
	ADDLW	0xF6	;Check for gain over 40
	BTFSC	STATUS,CARRY	
	CALL	DOT2	
	MOVF	STORE,0	;Place conversion in W
	BCF	STATUS,CARRY	
	ADDLW	0xF1	;Check for gain over 60
	BTFSC	STATUS,CARRY	
	CALL	DOT3	
	MOVF	STORE,0	;Place conversion in W
	BCF	STATUS,CARRY	
	ADDLW	0xE7	;Check for gain over 100
	BTFSC	STATUS,CARRY	
	CALL	DOT4	

```
          MOVF     STORE,0    ;Place conversion in W
          BCF      STATUS,CARRY
          ADDLW    0xCE       ;Check for gain over 200
          BTFSC    STATUS,CARRY
          CALL     DOT5
          MOVF     STORE,0    ;Place conversion in W
          BCF      STATUS,CARRY
          ADDLW    0xB5       ;Check for gain over 300
          BTFSC    STATUS,CARRY
          CALL     DOT6
          MOVF     STORE,0    ;Place conversion in W
          BCF      STATUS,CARRY
          ADDLW    9C         ;Check for gain over 400
          BTFSC    STATUS,CARRY
          CALL     DOT7
          MOVF     STORE,0    ;Place conversion in W
          BCF      STATUS,CARRY
          ADDLW    83         ;Check for gain over 500
          BTFSC    STATUS,CARRY
          CALL     DOT8
          MOVF     STORE,0    ;Place conversion in W
          BCF      STATUS,CARRY
          ADDLW    6A         ;Check for gain over 600
          BTFSC    STATUS,CARRY
          CALL     DOT9
          MOVF     STORE,0    ;Place conversion in W
          BCF      STATUS,CARRY
          ADDLW    38         ;Check for gain over 800
          BTFSC    STATUS,CARRY
          CALL     DOT10
          MOVF     DOTS,0
          MOVWF    PORTB
          MOVF     DOTS2,0
          MOVWF    PORTA
          CLRF     DOTS
          CLRF     DOTS2
          GOTO     LOOP
DOT1      MOVLW    01
          MOVWF    DOTS
          RETURN
```

```
DOT2      MOVLW      02
          MOVWF      DOTS
          RETURN
DOT3      MOVLW      04
          MOVWF      DOTS
          RETURN
DOT4      MOVLW      08
          MOVWF      DOTS
          RETURN
DOT5      MOVLW      10
          MOVWF      DOTS
          RETURN
DOT6      MOVLW      20
          MOVWF      DOTS
          RETURN
DOT7      MOVLW      40
          MOVWF      DOTS
          RETURN
DOT8      MOVLW      80
          MOVWF      DOTS
          RETURN
DOT9      CLRF       DOTS
          MOVLW      04
          MOVWF      DOTS2
          RETURN
DOT10     MOVLW      08
          MOVWF      DOTS2
          RETURN
          END
```

Components for Transistor Tester – 1 (Figures 1.11 and 1.12)

Resistors (all 0.25 watt 5% carbon film)
R1	22k
R2	2M2
R3	360k
R4, R5	390R (2 off)
R6 to R15	270R (10 off)
R16	390R

Capacitors

C1	10μ 25V elect
C2	220n polyester
C3, C4	100n ceramic
C5	220p polystyrene or ceramic plate

Semiconductors

IC1	TLC555CP
IC2	μA78L05 (+5V 100mA regulator)
IC3	PIC 16C71-04
TR1, TR2	BC560 (2 off)
D1 to D10	5mm red LED (10 off)

Miscellaneous

S1	s.p.s.t. min toggle switch
B1	9V (PP3 size)
SK1, SK2	Transistor holder (2 off)

Case, circuit board, 8-pin DIL holder, 18-pin DIL holder, battery connector, test leads, wire, solder, etc.

Transistor Tester – 2

This transistor tester is similar to the one described in the previous section of this book, but it has conventional PNP/NPN switching, and the current gain is shown on a two-digit display. Current gains of 10 to 990 can be accommodated, with a display resolution of 10. The figure on the display is actually one-tenth of the test device's current gain. For example, a reading of '52' actually indicates a current gain of 520. Obviously it is not difficult to mentally convert display readings into corresponding current gain, but a third digit which always reads zero can be added at the right hand end of the display if preferred, so that the displayed figure is the true current gain of the test component.

The circuit diagram for the 'improved' transistor tester appears in Figures 1.14 to 1.17. Figure 1.14 shows the circuit for the 5-volt regulator and input stages of the tester. The basic method of testing is much the same as for the original version, but the base of the test device is not driven from the output of a low frequency oscillator. Instead it is simply wired to the 0

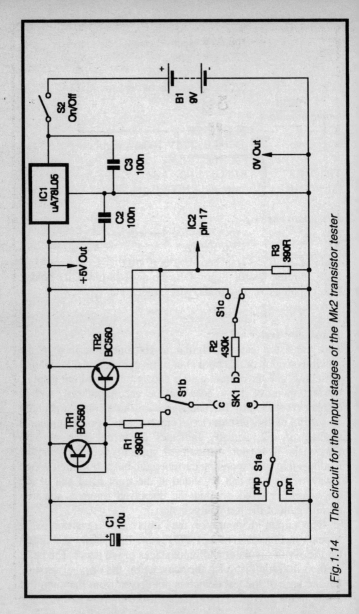

Fig. 1.14   The circuit for the input stages of the Mk2 transistor tester.

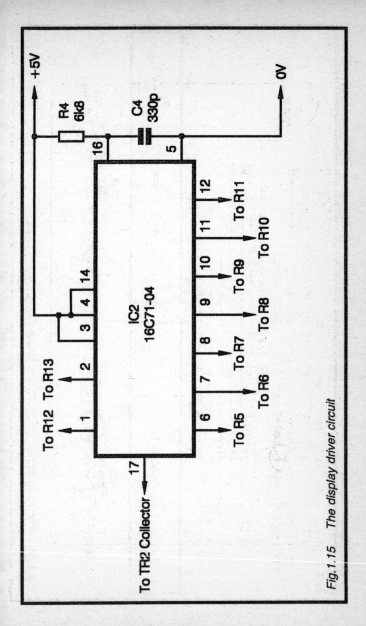

Fig. 1.15   The display driver circuit

45

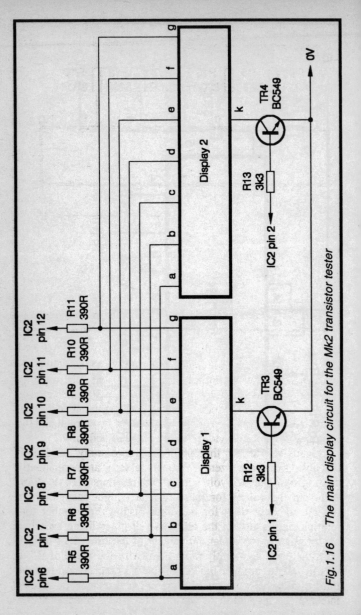

Fig. 1.16   The main display circuit for the Mk2 transistor tester

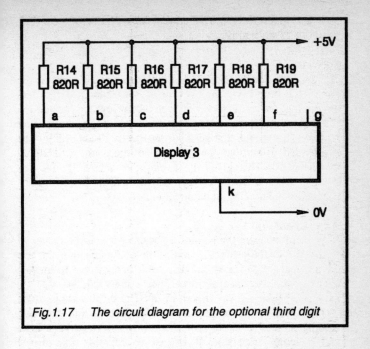

Fig.1.17   *The circuit diagram for the optional third digit*

volt or +5 volt supply rail via R2 and one pole of the PNP/NPN switch (S1c). The circuits of Figures 1.15 and 1.16 together form a simple two-digit voltmeter. This is basically the same as the one featured in Chapter 3. Refer to the relevant section of Chapter 3 if you require a description of how this circuit and the matching software provide a basic voltmeter action.

Figure 1.17 shows the circuit for the 'dummy' third digit that always displays a zero. Segments 'a' to 'f' are permanently driven from the +5 volt supply via resistors R14 to R19. Although the values for these resistors might seem high in relation to those used for the other displays, remember that multiplexing results in the other two displays being switched off for slightly more than 50 percent of the time. R14 to R19 must therefore be slightly more than twice the value of R5 to R11 in order to produce uniform display brightness. Adding the third digit gives a neater display, but it does not, of course, increase the resolution of the display, which remains at 10.

Note also that it increases the current consumption of the circuit by about 23 milliamps.

Software

The program for this project is fundamentally the same as the one for the simple two-digit voltmeter (see Chapter 3). It differs only in that once a reading has been taken from the converter a rotate right instruction is used to effectively divide the reading by two. This means that an input sensitivity of about 3.9 volts is provided, rather than the 1.96 volts of the voltmeter featured in Chapter 3. This gives the appropriate sensitivity for this design, with a collector current of about 10 milliamps producing the maximum gain reading of 990.

Adjustment and Use

In order to measure the gain of a transistor it is just a matter of setting S1 to the correct operating mode, connecting the test device, and then reading the display. It is advisable to make a check with the base terminal not connected, so that an excessive leakage level will show up. The display should read '00' (or '000') with the base lead not connected, and any other reading almost certainly indicates an excessive leakage level and a faulty transistor. It is just conceivable that a test component could have a gain of more than 990, which would give an overload ('–') warning on the display. This is unlikely though, and an overload warning is more likely to indicate a short-circuited device rather than one that has an ultra-high current gain. Disconnecting the base lead should result in a reading of zero on the display, and the transistor under test is certainly faulty if the overload warning remains.

```
'*************************************************
;Twin 7-Segment Display Transistor Tester Program
;*************************************************
;
STATUS      EQU       03
CARRY       EQU       00
ADIR        EQU       05
BDIR        EQU       06
ADCON       EQU       08
```

48

PORTA	EQU	05	
PORTB	EQU	06	
ADRES	EQU	09	
PC	EQU	02	
LNIBL	EQU	0C	
HNIBL	EQU	0D	
STORE	EQU	0E	
CNTR	EQU	0F	
	BSF	STATUS,5	;Select page 1
	CLRF	BDIR	;Set port B outputs
	MOVLW	0xF3	
	MOVWF	ADIR	;Set RA2/3 as digital lines
	MOVLW	02	
	MOVWF	ADCON	;Set RA0/1 as analogue inputs
	BCF	STATUS,5	;Select page 0
	MOVLW	0xC1	
	MOVWF	ADCON	;Select Ch0/Internal clock
MAIN	BSF	ADCON,2	;Start conversion
	NOP		;Wait
	MOVF	ADRES,0	;Place conversion in W
	MOVWF	STORE	;Store conversion
	RRF	STORE,1	;Divide conversion by two
	MOVF	STORE,0	
	BCF	STATUS,CARRY	
	SUBLW	63	
	BTFSS	STATUS,CARRY	
	GOTO	OVERLD	;Indicate overload if over 99
	MOVF	STORE,0	
	CALL	TABLE	;Convert to BCD
	MOVWF	LNIBL	
	MOVWF	HNIBL	
	RRF	HNIBL,1	
	RRF	HNIBL,1	
	RRF	HNIBL,1	
	RRF	HNIBL,1	;Shift high nibble into low one
	MOVLW	0F	
	ANDWF	HNIBL,1	;Mask high nibble of HNIBL
	ANDWF	LNIBL,1	;Mask high nibble of LNIBL
	MOVF	HNIBL,0	
	CALL	TABLE2	

49

```
              MOVWF      PORTB      ;Load high nibble into port B
              BSF        PORTA,2    ;Switch on 1st digit
              MOVLW      0xFF
              MOVWF      CNTR
DELAY1        DECFSZ     CNTR,1
              GOTO       DELAY1
              BCF        PORTA,2    ;Delay and switch off 1st digit
              MOVF       LNIBL,0
              CALL       TABLE2
              MOVWF      PORTB      ;Load low nibble into port B
              BSF        PORTA,3    ;Switch on 2nd digit
              MOVLW      0xFF
              MOVWF      CNTR
DELAY2        DECFSZ     CNTR,1
              GOTO       DELAY2     ;Delay and switch off 2nd digit
              BCF        PORTA,3    ;Switch off 2nd digit
              GOTO       MAIN       ;Repeat indefinitely
;
OVERLD        MOVLW      40
              MOVWF      PORTB      ;Load – into port B
              BSF        PORTA,2    ;Switch on 1st digit
              MOVLW      0xFF
              MOVWF      CNTR
DELAY3        DECFSZ     CNTR,1
              GOTO       DELAY3
              BCF        PORTA,2    ;Delay and switch off 1st digit
              BSF        PORTA,3    ;Switch on 2nd digit
              MOVLW      0xFF
              MOWF       CNTR
DELAY4        DECFSZ     CNTR,1
              GOTO       DELAY4     ;Delay and switch off 2nd digit
              BCF        PORTA,3    ;Switch off 2nd digit
              GOTO       MAIN       ;Return to main routine
;
TABLE         ADDWF      PC,1
              RETLW      00
              RETLW      01
              RETLW      02
              RETLW      03
              RETLW      04
```

RETLW	05
RETLW	06
RETLW	07
RETLW	08
RETLW	09
RETLW	10
RETLW	11
RETLW	12
RETLW	13
RETLW	14
RETLW	15
RETLW	16
RETLW	17
RETLW	18
RETLW	19
RETLW	20
RETLW	21
RETLW	22
RETLW	23
RETLW	24
RETLW	25
RETLW	26
RETLW	27
RETLW	28
RETLW	29
RETLW	30
RETLW	31
RETLW	32
RETLW	33
RETLW	34
RETLW	35
RETLW	36
RETLW	37
RETLW	38
RETLW	39
RETLW	40
RETLW	41
RETLW	42
RETLW	43
RETLW	44

```
RETLW    45
RETLW    46
RETLW    47
RETLW    48
RETLW    49
RETLW    50
RETLW    51
RETLW    52
RETLW    53
RETLW    54
RETLW    55
RETLW    56
RETLW    57
RETLW    58
RETLW    59
RETLW    60
RETLW    61
RETLW    62
RETLW    63
RETLW    64
RETLW    65
RETLW    66
RETLW    67
RETLW    68
RETLW    69
RETLW    70
RETLW    71
RETLW    72
RETLW    73
RETLW    74
RETLW    75
RETLW    76
RETLW    77
RETLW    78
RETLW    79
RETLW    80
RETLW    81
RETLW    82
RETLW    83
RETLW    84
```

```
        RETLW    85
        RETLW    86
        RETLW    87
        RETLW    88
        RETLW    89
        RETLW    90
        RETLW    91
        RETLW    92
        RETLW    93
        RETLW    94
        RETLW    95
        RETLW    96
        RETLW    97
        RETLW    98
        RETLW    99
;
TABLE2  ADDWF    PC,1
        RETLW    3F
        RETLW    06
        RETLW    5B
        RETLW    4F
        RETLW    66
        RETLW    6D
        RETLW    7D
        RETLW    07
        RETLW    7F
        RETLW    6F
        END
```

Components for Transistor Tester – 2
(Figures 1.14, 1.15, 1.16 and 1.17)

Resistors (all 0.25 watt 5% carbon film)
R1, R3   390R (2 off)
R2   430k
R4   6k8
R5 to R11   390R (7 off)
R12, R13   3k3 (2 off)
R14 to R19   820R (6 off)

Capacitors

C1	10μ 25V elect
C2, C3	100n ceramic (2 off)
C4	330p polystyrene or ceramic plate

Semiconductors

IC1	μA78L05 (+5V 100mA regulator)
IC2	16C71-04
TR1, TR2	BC560 (2 off)
TR3, TR4	BC549 (2 off)
Display 1, 2, 3	7-segment common cathode display (3 off)

Miscellaneous

S1	2-way 3-pole rotary switch
S2	s.p.s.t. min toggle switch
B1	9V (6 × AA size cells in holder)
SK1	transistor holder

Case, circuit board, 18-pin DIL holder, battery connector (PP3 type), wire, solder, etc.

Capacitance Checker

This simple capacitance checker has a two-digit display and four measuring ranges with full-scale values of 9.9n, 99n, 0.99μ, and 9.9μ. Obviously a two-digit display limits the accuracy of the unit, but it is adequate for many purposes. The resolution of a two-digit display is certainly equal to or better than the resolution offered by a small panel meter. An additional range with a full-scale value of 0.99n (990p) can be included if desired, but stray capacitance and other problems mean that accuracy on this range will not be quite as good as on the other ranges. Polarised (electrolytic, etc.) and non-polarised capacitors can be tested.

System Operation

The block diagram of Figure 1.18 helps to explain the basic way in which the capacitor checker functions. The PIC processor does little more than operate as a two-digit counter

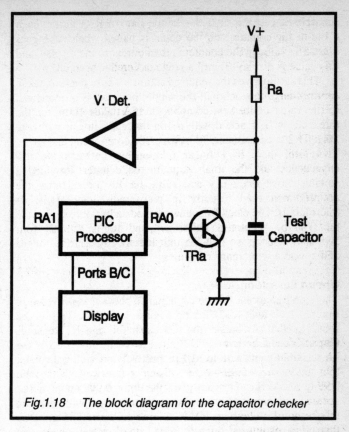

Fig.1.18   The block diagram for the capacitor checker

driving a two-digit seven-segment LED display. Ports B and C
of the PIC 16C55 drive the display that is not multiplexed. The
PIC processor provides what is effectively a small amount of
control logic, with RA0 operating as an output and RA1 acting
as an input. At the start of a measuring cycle RA0 is set high,
which turns on TRa and discharges the test capacitor. When
RA0 is set low, the capacitor starts to charge from the +5 volt
supply via resistor Ra, and the counter starts to count upwards
from zero. A voltage comparator monitors the charge on the
capacitor, and the output of the comparator will go high when
the charge voltage reaches half the supply potential. The

software detects this as it checks the state of RA1 during each cycle of the counter, and the count is halted when RA1 goes high. The value in the counter is then output to the display, and this value is displayed until a new reading has been taken.

This set-up gives the required action because the time taken for the charge to reach half the supply potential is proportional to the value of the test component. If it takes 10ms for the threshold to be reached with a 10n test capacitor, it will take 20ns for 20n component, 30ms for a 30n component, and so on. Therefore, there is a linear relationship between the test capacitance and the final value in the counter. Provided a suitable clock frequency and value for Ra are selected, the counter will read directly in picofarads, nanofarads, or microfarads. The clock frequency is made adjustable so that the unit can be accurately calibrated, and Ra is actually four switched resistors so that the unit has four measuring ranges and covers a wide range of values.

Circuit Operation

The circuit diagram for the capacitance checker is provided in Figures 1.19 and 1.20. Taking Figure 1.19 first, TR1 is the transistor that discharges the test capacitor, and R17 ensures that the discharge current is limited to a safe level. S2 is the range switch, with R18 to R21 respectively providing the 9.9n, 99n, 0.99μ, and 9.9μ ranges. Using a five-way switch and adding a 10M range resistor gives the unit a 0.99n range, but as pointed out previously, stray capacitance, etc., will result in relatively poor accuracy. IC3 is an operational amplifier, but in this circuit it is used open loop and it effectively becomes a voltage comparator. R23 and R24 provide a reference potential of 2.5 volts to the inverting input of IC3. The voltage on the test capacitor is fed to the non-inverting input via protection resistor R22. Note that IC3 must be an operational amplifier that will work well using a 5-volt supply, and that most types will not work properly in this circuit. It must also have a very high input resistance, and the CMOS input stage of the CA3130E ensures that it is more than adequate in this respect.

Turning now to Figure 1.20, this is the circuit diagram for the PIC processor and display stages. The common cathode LED displays are driven from the seven least significant bits of

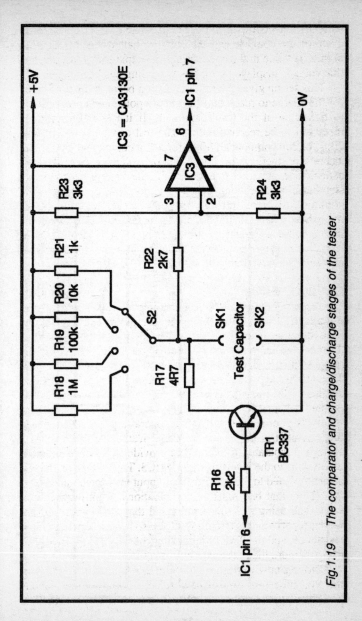

Fig. 1.19 The comparator and charge/discharge stages of the tester

57

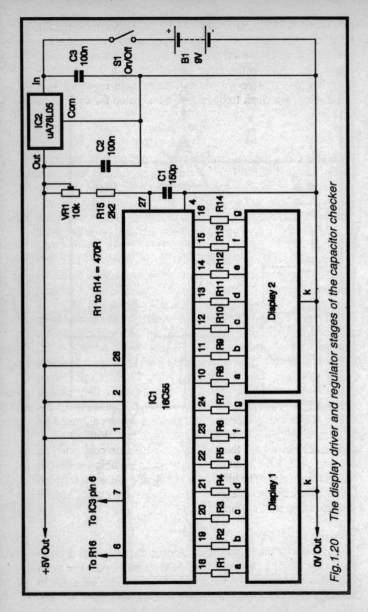

Fig. 1.20   The display driver and regulator stages of the capacitor checker

58

ports B and C of IC1. Displays 1 and 2 are respectively the left and right hand digits. A C-R clock just about gives adequate stability, but only if the circuit is powered from a well stabilised supply. The circuit is therefore powered from a 9-volt battery supply by way of five-volt monolithic voltage regulator IC2. VR1 enables the clock frequency to be adjusted for calibration purposes.

In Use

When using any capacitance-measuring device it is important that a charged capacitor is not connected to the unit. Particularly when testing higher voltage components, there is a risk that the charge on the component could damage the capacitance meter. It is probably worthwhile adding two extra one millimetre sockets on the front of the unit, with a resistor or about 100R in value connected across them. Test components can then be connected across these sockets and discharged prior to connecting them to SK1 and SK2. Note that polarised components must be tested with the positive lead connected to SK1 and the negative lead connected to SK2.

The unit can not be used in earnest until it has been calibrated. Calibration can be carried out on any range, and a capacitor having a value equal to about 50 to 100 percent of the full-scale value is required. The calibration capacitor should be a close tolerance (one or two percent) type. High value close tolerance capacitors are extremely expensive, if they can be obtained at all. Realistically, the unit has to be calibrated on the 9.9n or 99n range. Suppose that the unit is to be calibrated on the 9.9n range using a 6n8 calibrator capacitor. With S2 set to the correct range and the calibration capacitor connected to SK1 and SK2, VR1 is adjusted to produce a stable reading of '68' on the display. The unit is then ready for use, and provided R18 to R21 are close tolerance resistors, good accuracy should be obtained on all four ranges.

Software

The software for the capacitance checker starts by setting ports B and C as outputs, and it also sets RA0 as an output. The main program loop then provides a long output pulse on RA0 to discharge the test capacitor. This pulse is also used to slow down the rate at which readings are taken so that the display does not become ambiguous if the right-hand digit tends to alternate between two values. Once the discharge pulse has ended there is a brief delay before the counting action commences. This delay is needed to provide the correct counting action, and without it the minimum display reading would be '01' rather than '00'. Next the register, which contains the low nibble of the count ('LNIBL') is incremented, and then line RA1 is tested to determine whether or not the test capacitor has reached the threshold charge potential. If it has, the program branches to the subprogram called 'DISPLAY'. Here the BCD count is converted into data for the displays using the lookup table method, and then it is output to ports B and C. The count is kept in BCD (binary coded decimal) form rather than pure binary because it is easier to convert BCD data into the two seven-bit codes for the displays.

With a capacitor in circuit the charge will not have reached the threshold level at this stage, and the program therefore continues to perform the main loop. This tests to see if the low nibble has reached a value of 0A (10 decimal), and calls subroutine 'PLUSH' if it has. This routine zeros the low nibble counter and increments the high nibble counter ('HNIBL'). The main loop then continues with a check to determine whether or not the high nibble has reached 0A. If it has, the subprogram called 'OVER' is executed, and this writes a value of 40 (hex) to both displays. This produces an '–' overload warning on the display. The program goes back to the beginning of the main loop if no overload is detected, the low nibble is incremented, and so on. In this way the count steadily builds up until the capacitor reaches the half supply threshold level, and the value in the counter is then displayed.

```
;************************************************
;Capacitance Checker Program
;Least Significant Digit on RB0 TO RB6
;Most Significant Digit on RC0 TO RC6
;************************************************
;
;
STATUS      EQU        03
Z           EQU        02
```

```
C          EQU      0
LNIBL      EQU      0A
HNIBL      EQU      0B
CNTR       EQU      0E
CNTR2      EQU      0F
PORTA      EQU      05
PORTB      EQU      06
PORTC      EQU      07
PC         EQU      02
           CLRW
           TRIS     06          ;Set Port B as outputs
           TRIS     07          ;Set Port C as outputs
           MOVLW    0xFE
           TRIS     05          ;Set RA0 as an output
           CLRW
           MOVWF    LNIBL
           MOVWF    HNIBL
MAIN       BSF      PORTA,0     ;Start discharge pulse
           MOVLW    0xFF
           MOVWF    CNTR
           MOVLW    04
           MOVWF    CNTR2
DELAY      DECFSZ   CNTR,1
           GOTO     DELAY
           DECFSZ   CNTR2,1
           GOTO     DELAY
           BCF      PORTA,0     ;End discharge pulse
           MOVLW    04
           MOVWF    CNTR
DELAY2     DECFSZ   CNTR,1
           GOTO     DELAY2      ;Delay before testing capacitor
LOOP       BTFSC    PORTA,1
           GOTO     DISPLAY     ;Branch if capacitor fully charged
           MOVF     LNIBL,W
           BCF      STATUS,Z
           XORLW    0A
           BTFSC    STATUS,Z    ;Check if low nibble reached 10
           CALL     PLUSH       ;Zero and INC high nibble if it is
           MOVF     HNIBL,W
           BCF      STATUS,Z
```

61

```
          XORLW     0A
          BTFSC     STATUS,Z    ;Check if high nibble reached 10
          GOTO      OVER        ;Branch if it has
          INCF      LNIBL,1     ;Increment counter
          GOTO      LOOP
;
OVER      MOVLW     40
          MOVWF     PORTB
          MOVWF     PORTC
          CLRF      LNIBL
          CLRF      HNIBL
          GOTO      MAIN
;
PLUSH     INCF      HNIBL
          CLRF      LNIBL
          RETLW     00
;
DISPLAY
          MOVF      LNIBL,W
          CALL      TABLE       ;Load W with display data
          MOVWF     PORTB       ;Output data to port B
          MOVF      HNIBL,W
          CALL      TABLE       ;Load W with display data
          MOVWF     PORTC       ;Output data to Port C
          CLRF      LNIBL
          CLRF      HNIBL
          GOTO      MAIN        ;Clear counters and start new
                                 reading
;
TABLE     ADDWF     PC,1
          RETLW     3F
          RETLW     06
          RETLW     5B
          RETLW     4F
          RETLW     66
          RETLW     6D
          RETLW     7D
          RETLW     07
          RETLW     7F
          RETLW     6F
          END
```

Components for Capacitor Checker (Figures 1.19 and 1.20)

Resistors (all 0.25 watt 5% carbon film unless noted)
R1 to R14	470R (14 off)
R15, R16	2k2 (2 off)
R17	4R7
R18	1M 1%
R19	100k 1%
R20	10k 1%
R21	1k 1%
R22	2k7
R23, R24	3k3 (2 off)

Potentiometer
VR1	10k min hor preset

Capacitors
C1	150p polystyrene
C2, C3	100n ceramic (2 off)

Semiconductors
IC1	16C55-RC/P
IC2	µA78L05 (+5V 100mA regulator)
IC3	CA3130E
TR1	BC337
Display 1, 2	7-segment common cathode display (2 off)

Miscellaneous
B1	9V (6 × AA size cells in holder)
S1	s.p.s.t. min toggle
S2	4-way 3-pole rotary (only one pole used)
SK1	Red 1mm socket
SK2	Black 1mm socket

Case, component panel, 8-pin DIL holder, 28-pin DIL holder, control knob, battery connector (PP3 type), wire, solder, etc.

Chapter 2

GAMES AND NOVELTIES

8-Station Quiz Monitor

This unit is a monitor for television style quizzes where the first contestant to press his or her pushbutton gets the first chance at answering the question. It has eight pushbutton switches, with each of these operating its own LED indicator light. Operating one of the switches results in the corresponding LED switching on, and all the other indicator lights are then blocked. The display therefore indicates which contestant operated their pushbutton first and which one has won the chance to answer the question. Obviously a unit of this type cannot operate at an infinitely fast speed, and it is actually possible for the person who pushed second to 'win'. However, the pushbutton switches are scanned at a very high rate, and even a difference of a few microseconds is sufficient to ensure that the right result is produced. In practice the unit should always produce a valid indication.

Circuit Operation

The full circuit diagram for the eight-station quiz monitor appears in Figure 2.1. The use of a PIC processor enables an extremely simple circuit to be used, and the unit consists of little more than the eight pushbutton switches, the eight indicator LEDs, and the PIC processor itself. The switches are read by port B, and the display is driven from port C. As more than twelve input and output lines are needed the circuit is based on a 16C55, which has an ample 20 lines in total. In fact three lines of port A are left unused.

The pushbutton switches are S1 to S8, and the eight indicators LEDs are D1 to D8. The eight input lines that monitor the switches have pull-up resistors (R1 to R8), and operating one of the pushbutton switches therefore pulls the corresponding input line low. The eight LEDs are driven at a fairly high current of about 20 milliamps, which gives very good brightness from large high efficiency LEDs. There is no problem in using an output current of 20 milliamps since only

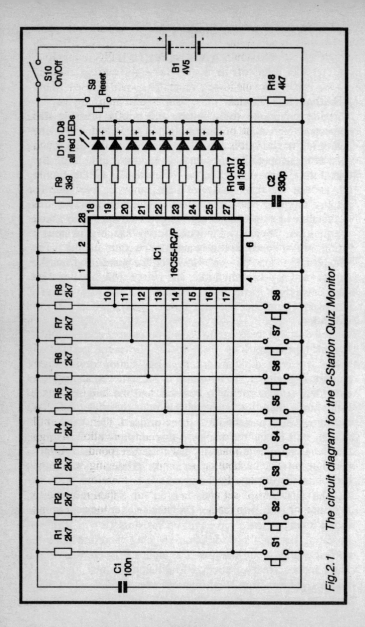

Fig.2.1   The circuit diagram for the 8-Station Quiz Monitor

66

one LED at the time will be switched on, and the total port current will therefore be 20 milliamps as well. Note that 20 milliamps is the maximum output current for a PIC output line, and that the value of 150R for the eight current limiting resistors is therefore the lowest value that should be used. Many LEDs are not rated to take more than 20 milliamps anyway.

Switch S9 is the reset button, and briefly pressing this switch pulls an input of port A (RA0) high and clears the display so that the unit is ready to adjudicate on the next round of button pushing. The internal C-R clock circuit of the processor is used, and this has R9 and C2 as the timing components. A fairly high clock frequency is used as this enables the unit to scan the switches at a high rate, and ensures fair results. The current consumption of the circuit is only about 2 milliamps under standby conditions, but this obviously increases by about 20 milliamps when one of the LED indicators is active. This gives an extremely long life from the 4.5-volt battery pack, which consists of three AA size batteries in a plastic holder.

Software

The initial part of the program sets up port C as a eight outputs. The main program loop then checks the eight pushbutton switches in turn, and if one has been operated the appropriate subroutine is called up. The subroutines output the appropriate values to port C, so that the correct LED is switched on when a pushbutton switch is activated. Once the appropriate LED has been activated it is essential that the program then halts until the reset switch is activated. If the program were allowed to go straight back into the main loop it would respond to further operations of the pushbutton switches, producing unwanted changes in the display. Each subroutine is therefore made to loop until line RA0 is set and the program is then returned to the main loop. It is then ready to adjudicate over the next round of questioning.

```
;*************************************************
;Eight Station Quiz Monitor Program
;*************************************************
;
PORTA     EQU     05
PORTB     EQU     06
PORTC     EQU     07
          CLRW
          TRIS    07        ;Sets Port C as outputs
          MOVLW   00
          MOVWF   PORTC     ;Switches off display initially
LOOP      BTFSS   PORTB,0   ;Check setting of S1
          CALL    PLYR1
          BTFSS   PORTB,1   ;Check setting of S2
          CALL    PLYR2
          BTFSS   PORTB,2   ;Check setting of S3
          CALL    PLYR3
          BTFSS   PORTB,3   ;Check setting of S4
          CALL    PLYR4
          BTFSS   PORTB,4   ;Check setting of S5
          CALL    PLYR5
          BTFSS   PORTB,5   ;Check setting of S6
          CALL    PLYR6
          BTFSS   PORTB,6   ;Check setting of S7
          CALL    PLYR7
          BTFSS   PORTB,7   ;Check setting of S8
          CALL    PLYR8
          GOTO    LOOP      ;Read switches indefinitely
PLYR1     MOVLW   01
          MOVWF   PORTC     ;Switch on D1
RESET1    BTFSS   PORTA,0   ;Wait for reset
          GOTO    RESET1
          MOVLW   00
          MOVWF   PORTC     ;Switch off display
          RETLW   00
PLYR2     MOVLW   02
          MOVWF   PORTC     ;Switch on D2
RESET2    BTFSS   PORTA,0   ;Wait for reset
          GOTO    RESET2
          MOVLW   00
```

	MOVWF	PORTC	;Switch off display
	RETLW	00	
PLYR3	MOVLW	04	
	MOVWF	PORTC	;Switch on D3
RESET3	BTFSS	PORTA,0	;Wait for reset
	GOTO	RESET3	
	MOVLW	00	
	MOVWF	PORTC	;Switch off display
	RETLW	00	
PLYR4	MOVLW	08	
	MOVWF	PORTC	;Switch on D4
RESET4	BTFSS	PORTA,0	;Wait for reset
	GOTO	RESET4	
	MOVLW	00	
	MOVWF	PORTC	;Switch off display
	RETLW	00	
PLYR5	MOVLW	10	
	MOVWF	PORTC	;Switch on D5
RESET5	BTFSS	PORTA,0	;Wait for reset
	GOTO	RESET5	
	MOVLW	00	
	MOVWF	PORTC	;Switch off display
	RETLW	00	
PLYR6	MOVLW	20	
	MOVWF	PORTC	;Switch on D6
RESET6	BTFSS	PORTA,0	;Wait for reset
	GOTO	RESET6	
	MOVLW	00	
	MOVWF	PORTC	;Switch off display
	RETLW	00	
PLYR7	MOVLW	40	
	MOVWF	PORTC	;Switch on D7
RESET7	BTFSS	PORTA,0	;Wait for reset
	GOTO	RESET7	
	MOVLW	00	
	MOVWF	PORTC	;Switch off display
	RETLW	00	
PLYR8	MOVLW	80	
	MOVWF	PORTC	;Switch on D8
RESET8	BTFSS	PORTA,0	;Wait for reset

```
GOTO      RESET8
MOVLW     00
MOVWF     PORTC      ;Switch off display
RETLW     00
END
```

Components for 8 Station Quiz Monitor (Figure 2.1)

Resistors (all 0.25 watt 5% carbon film)
R1 to R8	2k7 (8 off)
R9	3k9
R10 to R17	150R (8 off)
R18	4k7

Capacitors
C1	100n ceramic
C2	330p polystyrene

Semiconductors
IC1	PIC 16C55-RC/P
D1 to D8	8mm or 10mm diameter high brightness red LEDs (8 off)

Miscellaneous
S1 to S9	Push-to-make switches (9 off)
S10	s.p.s.t. min toggle
B1	4.5V (3 × AA size cells in holder)

Circuit board, case, battery connector (PP3 type), 28 pin DIL holder, wire, solder, etc.

Quiz Monitor With Buzzer

This quiz monitor is much the same as the one described in the previous section of this chapter, but it has the added feature of a buzzer that sounds when a contestant operates his or her pushbutton. The 'buzz' continues until the quizmaster operates the reset button. An advantage of using microcontrollers is that it is often possible to add extra features with little extra hardware being required. The additional features can be largely implemented in the software. The buzzer feature can in fact be

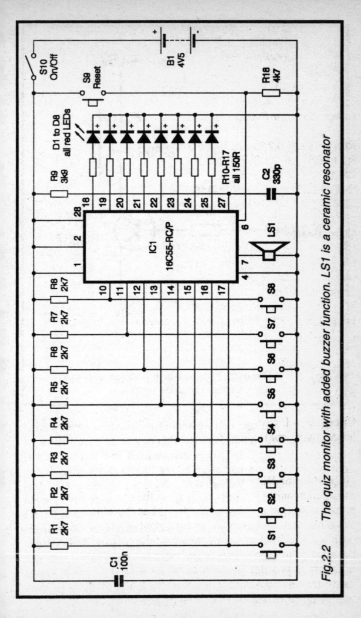

Fig.2.2   The quiz monitor with added buzzer function. LS1 is a ceramic resonator

71

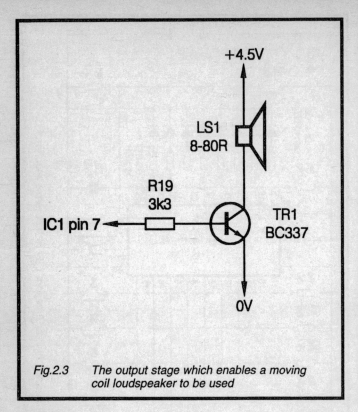

Fig.2.3   The output stage which enables a moving coil loudspeaker to be used

added using just one extra component, which is either a high impedance (64R to 80R) loudspeaker or a ceramic resonator, as shown in Figure 2.2. This is driven from line RA1 which is obviously set to operate as an output line. It is not advisable to use a moving coil loudspeaker having an impedance of less than 64R as this could result in a grossly excessive output current that could damage the PIC processor. While the buzzer is active there is an increase in the current consumption of the circuit, but this is not likely to be significant if a ceramic resonator is used. These are relatively efficient, and will probably boost the current drain by no more than a milliamp or two. Using a high impedance loudspeaker is likely to produce an increase of around 15 to 20 milliamps.

Due to the low drive current available, the volume obtained is not very high if the loudspeaker is driven direct from the PIC processor. This is not necessarily important, as in many cases high volume would simply make the 'buzz' more irksome rather than more effective. However, if the unit is used in a noisy environment a boost in the volume of the 'buzz' can be desirable. This can be achieved by using a moving coil loudspeaker driven via a single transistor amplifier. The circuit for this add-on amplifier appears in Figure 2.3. TR1 operates as a simple common emitter switching stage, which is driven from the output of the processor by way of current limiting resistor R19. The loudspeaker forms the collector load for TR1. When output RA1 goes high TR1 is switched on, and LS1 is effectively connected across the supply rails. When RA1 goes low TR1 is switched off, and no significant current is fed to LS1. This very basic method of driving the loudspeaker is perfectly acceptable in this application where only a simple pulse signal is involved. The loudspeaker can have an impedance in the range 8R to 80R, and low impedance loudspeakers give higher output powers. This is at the expense of higher current consumption though, and with an 8R loudspeaker the current drain can increase by as much as 200 milliamps when the buzzer operates.

Software

The program for this version of the quiz monitor is based on the software for the original design, but a substantial number of modifications have had to be made. Some additional setting up is required at the beginning of the program because line RA1 has to be set as an output. The other three lines of port A are left as inputs. Previously the display was cleared at the end of each subroutine just before the program returned to the main loop. In this program things are simplified by having the display cleared on each loop of the main program loop. This still ensures that the display is cleared almost at once when the reset button is operated, but it also means that there are numerous unnecessary write operations to port C as the program circulates around the main loops. These write operations slow things down very slightly, but otherwise have no significant affect.

The subroutines have been modified and extended to produce the pulses on RA1 that drive the loudspeaker. As the subroutines are essentially the same we will only consider the first of them (PLAYR1). As before, the appropriate LED of the display is switched on at the start of the routine. The reset switch is then checked, but this operates in a different fashion to the original program. If the reset switch is operated the program returns to the main loop, but otherwise it loops around the subroutine. The main section of the routine sets RA1 high and then holds it high while a delay loop is performed. RA1 is then set low again while a second delay loop is performed. This generates the required pulse train as the program loops around the subroutine, and the values used in the delay loop control the mark-space ratio and frequency of the 'buzz'. The sample values produce a squarewave output signal, with S1 to S4 producing a slightly lower frequency 'buzz' than S5 to S8. It is assumed here that the unit will be used with two teams of four players, and a different tone is therefore produced for each team. However, it is obviously possible to arrange things differently, with a different tone for each contestant if desired. It is just a matter of changing the values in the delay loops.

```
;************************************************
;Eight Station Quiz Monitor Program
;************************************************
;
PORTA       EQU      05
PORTB       EQU      06
PORTC       EQU      07
CNTR        EQU      0C
            CLRW
            TRIS     07           ;Sets Port C as outputs
            MOVLW    0D
            TRIS     05           ;Sets RA1 as an output
            MOVLW    00
            MOVWF    PORTC        ;Switches off display initially
LOOP        BTFSS    PORTB,0      ;Check setting of S1
            CALL     PLYR1
            BTFSS    PORTB,1      ;Check setting of S2
```

74

```
          CALL      PLYR2
          BTFSS     PORTB,2    ;Check setting of S3
          CALL      PLYR3
          BTFSS     PORTB,3    ;Check setting of S4
          CALL      PLYR4
          BTFSS     PORTB,4    ;Check setting of S5
          CALL      PLYR5
          BTFSS     PORTB,5    ;Check setting of S6
          CALL      PLYR6
          BTFSS     PORTB,6    ;Check setting of S7
          CALL      PLYR7
          BTFSS     PORTB,7    ;Check setting of S8
          CALL      PLYR8
          CLRW
          MOVWF     PORTC      ;Clears the display
          GOTO      LOOP       ;Read switches indefinitely
;
PLYR1     MOVLW     01
          MOVWF     PORTC      ;Switch on D1
RESET1    BTFSC     PORTA,0    ;Wait for reset
          RETLW     00         ;Return to main loop if reset
                               pressed
          MOVLW     02
          MOVWF     PORTA      ;Turn on speaker
          MOVLW     60         ;Hold speaker on for this No. of
                               loops
          MOVWF     CNTR
DELAY1    DECFSZ    CNTR,1
          GOTO      DELAY1
          CLRW
          MOVWF     PORTA      ;Switch speaker off
          MOVLW     60         ;Hold speaker off for this No. of
                               loops
          MOVWF     CNTR
DELAY2    DECFSZ    CNTR,1
          GOTO      DELAY2
          GOTO      RESET1
;
PLYR2     MOVLW     02
          MOVWF     PORTC      ;Switch on D2
```

75

```
RESET2    BTFSC    PORTA,0    ;Wait for reset
          RETLW 00
          MOVLW    02
          MOVWF    PORTA
          MOVLW    60
          MOVWF    CNTR
DELAY3    DECFSZ   CNTR,1
          GOTO     DELAY3
          CLRW
          MOVWF    PORTA
          MOVLW    60
          MOVWF    CNTR
DELAY4    DECFSZ   CNTR,1
          GOTO     DELAY4
          GOTO     RESET2
;
PLYR3     MOVLW    04
          MOVWF    PORTC      ;Switch on D3
RESET3    BTFSC    PORTA,0    ;Wait for reset
          RETLW    00
          MOVLW    02
          MOVWF    PORTA
          MOVLW    60
          MOVWF    CNTR
DELAY5    DECFSZ   CNTR,1
          GOTO     DELAY5
          CLRW
          MOVWF    PORTA
          MOVLW    60
          MOVWF    CNTR
DELAY6    DECFSZ   CNTR,1
          GOTO     DELAY6
          GOTO     RESET3
;
PLYR4     MOVLW    08
          MOVWF    PORTC      ;Switch on D4
RESET4    BTFSC    PORTA,0    ;Wait for reset
          RETLW    00
          MOVLW    02
          MOVWF    PORTA
```

```
          MOVLW     60
          MOVWF     CNTR
DELAY7    DECFSZ    CNTR,1
          GOTO      DELAY7
          CLRW
          MOVWF     PORTA
          MOVLW     60
          MOVWF     CNTR
DELAY8    DECFSZ    CNTR,1
          GOTO      DELAY8
          GOTO      RESET4
;
PLYR5     MOVLW     10
          MOVWF     PORTC     ;Switch on D5
RESET5    BTFSC     PORTA,0   ;Wait for reset
          RETLW     00
          MOVLW     02
          MOVWF     PORTA
          MOVLW     50
          MOVWF     CNTR
DELAY9    DECFSZ    CNTR,1
          GOTO      DELAY9
          CLRW
          MOVWF     PORTA
          MOVLW     50
          MOVWF     CNTR
DELAY10   DECFSZ    CNTR,1
          GOTO      DELAY10
          GOTO      RESET5
;
PLYR6     MOVLW     20
          MOVWF     PORTC     ;Switch on D6
RESET6    BTFSC     PORTA,0   ;Wait for reset
          RETLW     00
          MOVLW     02
          MOVWF     PORTA
          MOVLW     50
          MOVWF     CNTR
DELAY11   DECFSZ    CNTR,1
          GOTO      DELAY11
```

```
            CLRW
            MOVWF      PORTA
            MOVLW      50
            MOVWF      CNTR
DELAY12     DECFSZ     CNTR,1
            GOTO       DELAY12
            GOTO       RESET6
;
PLYR7       MOVLW      40
            MOVWF      PORTC       ;Switch on D7
RESET7      BTFSC      PORTA,0     ;Wait for reset
            RETLW      00
            MOVLW      02
            MOVWF      PORTA
            MOVLW      50
            MOVWF      CNTR
DELAY13     DECFSZ     CNTR,1
            GOTO       DELAY13
            CLRW
            MOVWF      PORTA
            MOVLW      50
            MOVWF      CNTR
DELAY14     DECFSZ     CNTR,1
            GOTO       DELAY14
            GOTO       RESET7
;
PLYR8       MOVLW      80
            MOVWF      PORTC       ;Switch on D8
RESET8      BTFSC      PORTA,0     ;Wait for reset
            RETLW      00
            MOVLW      02
            MOVWF      PORTA
            MOVLW      50
            MOVWF      CNTR
DELAY15     DECFSZ     CNTR,1
            GOTO       DELAY15
            CLRW
            MOVWF      PORTA
            MOVLW      50
            MOVWF      CNTR
```

```
DELAY16    DECFSZ    CNTR,1
           GOTO      DELAY16
           GOTO      RESET8
           END
```

Components For Quiz Monitor With Buzzer
(Figures 2.2 and 2.3)

Resistors (all 0.25 watt 5% carbon film)
R1 to R8   2k7 (8 off)
R9   3k9
R10 to R17   150R (8 off)
R18   4k7
R19   3k3

Capacitors
C1   100n ceramic
C2   330p polystyrene

Semiconductors
IC1   PIC 16C55-RC/P
TR1   BC337
D1 to D8   8mm or 10mm diameter high brightness red
               LEDs (8 off)

Miscellaneous
S1 to S9   Push-to-make switches (9 off)
S10   s.p.s.t. min toggle
B1   4.5V (3 × AA size cells in holder)
LS1   8 - 80R impedance moving coil loudspeaker
Circuit board, case, battery connector (PP3 type), 28-pin DIL
holder, wire, solder, etc.

If a ceramic resonator is used for LS1, omit TR1 and R19.

Electronic Die
The singular of dice is a die, and as this project produces a
simulation of a single die, it is therefore an electronic die rather
than an electronic dice. Using a PIC processor there is no

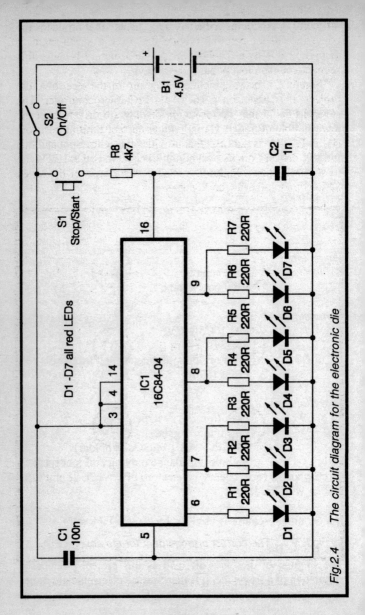

Fig.2.4   The circuit diagram for the electronic die

difficulty in producing a die having a display that produces the conventional dot patterns or one that uses a seven-segment display. A dot style display was selected merely because this seems to be the most popular these days.

Figure 2.4 shows the circuit diagram for the electronic die project. It is based on a 16C84-04 PIC microcontroller. The seven LEDs in the 'H' formation display are driven from the lower nibble of port B via individual current limiting resistors (R1 to R7). D1 is the LED that provides the centre spot and this must be driven from its own output line, but the other LEDs can be driven in pairs. Figure 2.5 shows where each of the seven LEDs fits into the 'H' configuration.

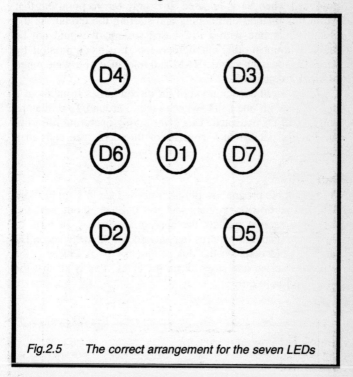

Fig.2.5   The correct arrangement for the seven LEDs

The basic action of the unit is to continuously cycle through the six displayable numbers at a very high rate. However, this only

81

occurs while S1 is pressed and the built-in C-R clock is functioning. When S1 is released the clock stops, and the display 'freezes' at whatever number it happened to be displaying at the instant the clock came to a halt. When S1 is operated again the circuit starts cycling through the six numbers once more, and this continues until S1 is released. As before, the display then halts at whatever number it was displaying when the clock stopped. Due to the high rate at which the circuit cycles the display, all the LEDs appear to be lit up continuously while the clock is running. It is totally impossible for the user to stop the clock when a particular number is displayed, and a random number from one to six is produced when S1 is released. It is only fair to point out that while this method of stopping and starting the circuit via the clock works fine with a PIC based system, it would not be viable with most other microprocessors. It is made possible by the PIC processor's static RAM and tolerance of a wide range of clock frequencies.

The current consumption of the circuit varies from about 7 milliamps with one LED switched on, to around 42 milliamps with six LEDs activated. This gives a long operating life from the battery pack, which consists of three AA size cells in a holder.

Software
A very simple program is all that is needed for this application. The first part of the program sets port B as an output port, and the main section outputs the appropriate values, in turn, to produce the six dot patterns (e.g. a value of 02 switches on D2 and D3, and displays the dot pattern for two). Because the action is started and stopped via the clock, this is all that the software has to do!

```
;************************************************;
; Simple Die Program
;************************************************
;
;
STATUS      EQU      03
BDIR        EQU      06
```

```
PORTB      EQU        06
BSF        STATUS,5                 ;Select page 1
CLRW
MOVWF      BDIR                     ;Set port B as outputs
BCF        STATUS,5                 ;Select page 0
MAIN       MOVLW      01
           MOVWF      PORTB         ;Display 1
           MOVLW      02
           MOVWF      PORTB         ;Display 2
           MOVLW      03
           MOVWF      PORTB         ;Display 3
           MOVLW      06
           MOVWF      PORTB         ;Display 4
           MOVLW      07
           MOVWF      PORTB         ;Display 5
           MOVLW      0E
           MOVWF      PORTB         ;Display 6
           GOTO       MAIN
           END
```

Components For Electronic Die (Figure 2.4)

Resistors (all 0.25 watt 5% carbon film)
R1 to R7   220R (7 off)
R8   4k7

Capacitors
C1   100n ceramic
C2   1n polyester

Semiconductors
IC1   PIC 16C84-04
D1 to D7   Red panel LEDs (7 off)

Miscellaneous
S1   Push-to-make switch
S2   s.p.s.t. min toggle switch
B1   4.5 volt (3 × AA size cells in holder)
Case, circuit board, PP3 battery connector, 18-pin DIL holder,
wire, solder, etc.

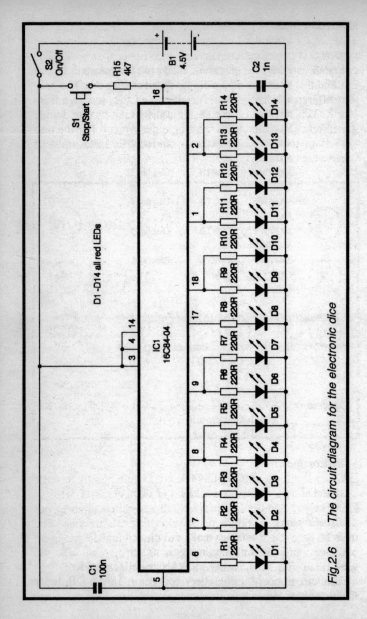

Fig.2.6   The circuit diagram for the electronic dice

Electronic Dice

This project is similar to the previous one, but it simulates two dice, and is therefore an electronic dice rather than a die. The circuit diagram for the electronic dice project appears in Figure 2.6, and this is similar to the circuit for the single die. The only real difference is that a second set of seven LEDs is driven from port A. This does, of course, result in the circuit having double the current consumption of the single die project. For the unit to produce the correct dot patterns the fourteen LEDs must be used in the configuration shown in Figure 2.7.

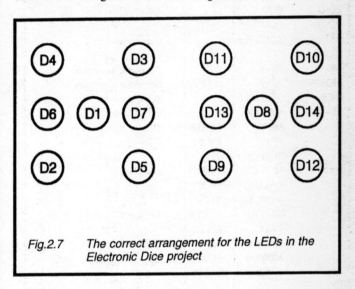

Fig.2.7   The correct arrangement for the LEDs in the
          Electronic Dice project

Software

Like the single die project, this one must cycle rapidly through all the possible combinations for the display. With what is effectively a two-digit display and six possible numbers per digit, this gives 36 values for the unit to cycle through. The main body of the program is similar to the original die program, but each time the display on port B is incremented, the subroutine (DICE2) is called. This subroutine cycles the display on port A through its six states, and this display therefore goes through its six states at each setting of the other

85

display. This gives the required cycling through all 36 possible states of the two digits.

```
;**************************************************
;Electronic Dice Program
;**************************************************
;
STATUS      EQU         03
BDIR        EQU         06
ADIR        EQU         05
PORTB       EQU         06
PORTA       EQU         05
BSF         STATUS,5                ;Select page 1
CLRW
MOVWF       BDIR            -       ;Set port B as outputs
MOVWF       ADIR                    ;Set port A as outputs
BCF         STATUS,5                ;Select page 0
MAIN        MOVLW       01
            MOVWF       PORTB       ;Display 1
            CALL        DICE2
            MOVLW       02
            MOVWF       PORTB       ;Display 2
            CALL        DICE2
            MOVLW       03
            MOVWF       PORTB       ;Display 3
            CALL        DICE2
            MOVLW       06
            MOVWF       PORTB       ;Display 4
            CALL        DICE2
            MOVLW       07
            MOVWF       PORTB       ;Display 5
            CALL        DICE2
            MOVLW       0E
            MOVWF       PORTB       ;Display 6
            CALL        DICE2
            GOTO        MAIN
;
DICE2       MOVLW       01
            MOVWF       PORTA       ;Display 1
            MOVLW       02
```

```
            MOVWF      PORTA      ;Display 2
            MOVLW      03
            MOVWF      PORTA      ;Display 3
            MOVLW      06
            MOVWF      PORTA      ;Display 4
            MOVLW      07
            MOVWF      PORTA      ;Display 5
            MOVLW      0E
            MOVWF      PORTA      ;Display 6
            RETURN
            END
```

Components for the Electronic Dice (Figure 2.6)

Resistors (all 0.25 watt 5% carbon film)
R1 to R14   220R (14 off)
R15   4k7

Capacitors
C1   100n ceramic
C2   1n polyester

Semiconductors
IC1   PIC 16C84-04
D1 to D14   Red panel LEDs (14 off)

Miscellaneous
S1   Push-to-make switch
S2   s.p.s.t. min toggle switch
B1   4.5 volt (3 × AA size cells in holder)
Case, circuit board, PP3 battery connector, 18-pin DIL holder,
wire, solder, etc.

Improvements

There is a slight flaw in both the die and dice programs in that
the displays show six dots for longer than any of the other dot
patterns. This occurs because of the GOTO instruction that
brings the program back to the beginning of the main loop so
that it loops indefinitely. Matters are made worse by the fact
that a GOTO instruction takes two cycles whereas the others

are single cycle instructions. This biasing towards a 'six' is not usually of any great importance as it is the same for all the players, but it can be removed by adding NOP instructions to equalise things. This is the equalised version of the electronic die program (the dice program could obviously be evened out in the same manner).

```
;**************************************************
;Simple Die Program
;**************************************************
;
STATUS      EQU         03
BDIR        EQU         06
PORTB       EQU         06
BSF         STATUS,5                ;Select page 1
CLRW
MOVWF       BDIR                    ;Set port B as outputs
BCF         STATUS,5                ;Select page 0
MAIN        MOVLW       01
            MOVWF       PORTB       ;Display 1
            NOP
            NOP
            MOVLW       02
            MOVWF       PORTB       ;Display 2
            NOP
            NOP
            MOVLW       03
            MOVWF       PORTB       ;Display 3
            NOP
            NOP
            MOVLW       06
            MOVWF       PORTB       ;Display 4
            NOP
            NOP
            MOVLW       07
            MOVWF       PORTB       ;Display 5
            NOP
            NOP
            MOVLW       0E
            MOVWF       PORTB       ;Display 6
```

Strength Meter

This is a not too serious attempt at a device for measuring the strength of one's grip. The basic idea is for the contestant to grip a piece of wood as hard as possible. This wooden handle is fitted with two electrodes, and the electronics in the device respond to the resistance across the electrodes. The measured 'strength' of the competitor is indicated by way of a nine-LED bargraph display. The harder the electrodes are gripped the lower the resistance across them, and the higher the indication on the display. If the electrodes are gripped hard enough the ninth LED switches off and an audio tone is produced, indicating that the contestant has achieved Superman status!

Obviously the way in which this unit functions is rather non-scientific, and is prone to errors. The main cause of erroneous results is variations in the skin resistance of the contestants. Someone who is very strong but has relatively thick and dry skin may struggle to produce a high score, as they will have a high skin resistance. On the other hand, someone who is relatively weak but has thin and moist skin may well be able to score well due to his or her low skin resistance. It is therefore not beyond the realms of possibility that a butch male could be outscored by a feeble female. However, as the unit is simply for fun, this could be regarded as an asset that increases its 'play' value.

Figure 2.8 shows the full circuit diagram for the strength meter, and this is very similar to the display circuit for the Transistor Tester project featured in chapter one. The only significant difference is that the tenth LED in the display has been omitted and replaced with LS1, which is a ceramic resonator. The circuit might work satisfactorily using high impedance moving coil loudspeaker for LS1, but it has not been tried with one. The pulses to produce the audio tone from LS1 are produced by the software.

On the input side of the circuit a potential divider is formed by the skin resistance across the electrodes and the series resistance of R1 and VR1. The lower the resistance across the

89

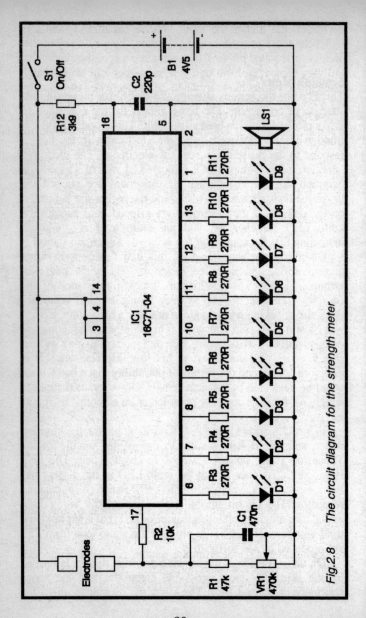

Fig.2.8   The circuit diagram for the strength meter

electrodes, the higher the input voltage fed to IC1, and the higher the score produced on the display. The sensitivity of the circuit is controlled by VR1. The effectiveness of the electrodes will vary somewhat from one unit to another, but VR1 should enable good results to be obtained using electrodes of virtually any size. Start with this control at a middle setting and then set it for a lower resistance if it is too easy to obtain a high score or a higher resistance if high scores prove to be impossible to produce. With a little trial and error a setting for VR1 that gives good results should soon be found. C1 should prevent problems with stray pickup of electrical noise producing unstable and ambiguous readings on the display.

A little ingenuity has to be used when designing the mechanical aspects of this project, as there is the handgrip and the electrodes to contend with. It is probably best if the handgrip is constructed as a separate piece and connected to the main unit by way of a twin cable about 0.5 metres long. The grip can be based on a piece of timber about 25 to 40 millimetres square and around 100 to 150 millimetres in length. Wood is not the best of electrical insulators but is perfectly adequate for this application. The electrodes do not have to be very large, and it may even be necessary to reduce the values of R1 and VR1 if they are each more than a few square centimetres in area.

Software

This program operates in a manner that is broadly the same as the one for the transistor tester described in chapter one. In fact the main program loop and most of the subroutines are the same, and it is only in the 'DOT10' subroutine that there is a significant difference. This routine has been changed so that it first clears the 'DOTS2' register to switch off the ninth LED in the display. It then places output line RA3 high, provides a delay, sets RA3 low again, provides a further delay, and then returns to the main program loop. This occurs on each loop of the main program while the input voltage is high enough, generating an audio tone from the ceramic resonator connected to RA3. The specified value in the delay loops produces a low to middle audio frequency from the resonator, but a wide range of frequencies can be obtained by using different values.

Longer delays provide lower output frequencies, and shorter delays give higher tones.

```
;************************************************
;Strength Meter Program
;************************************************
;
CARRY     EQU      00
DOTS      EQU      0E
DOTS2     EQU      0F
STATUS    EQU      03
ADIR      EQU      05
BDIR      EQU      06
ADCON     EQU      08
PORTA     EQU      05
PORTB     EQU      06
ADRES     EQU      09
STORE     EQU      0C
CNTR      EQU      0D
          BSF      STATUS,5      ;Select page 1
          MOVLW    0xF3
          MOVWF    ADIR          ;Sets RA2/3 as outputs
          CLRW
          MOVWF    BDIR          ;Sets Port B as outputs
          MOVLW    02
          MOVWF    ADCON         ;Sets RA0/1 as A/D inputs
          BCF      STATUS,5      ;Select page 0
          MOVLW    0xC1
          MOVWF    ADCON         ;Select Ch0/Int clock
LOOP      BSF      ADCON,2       ;Start conversion
          NOP                    ;Wait
          MOVF     ADRES,0       ;Place conversion in W
          MOVWF    STORE         ;Place conversion in STORE
          BCF      STATUS,CARRY
          ADDLW    0xF8          ;Check for gain over 20
          BTFSC    STATUS,CARRY
          CALL     DOT1
          MOVF     STORE,0       ;Place conversion in W
          BCF      STATUS,CARRY
          ADDLW    0xF6          ;Check for gain over 40
```

92

```
        BTFSC       STATUS,CARRY
        CALL        DOT2
        MOVF        STORE,0     ;Place conversion in W
        BCF         STATUS,CARRY
        ADDLW       0xF1        ;Check for gain over 60
        BTFSC       STATUS,CARRY
        CALL        DOT3
        MOVF        STORE,0     ;Place conversion in W
        BCF         STATUS,CARRY
        ADDLW       0xE7        ;Check for gain over 100
        BTFSC       STATUS,CARRY
        CALL        DOT4
        MOVF        STORE,0     ;Place conversion in W
        BCF         STATUS,CARRY
        ADDLW       0xCE        ;Check for gain over 200
        BTFSC       STATUS,CARRY
        CALL        DOT5
        MOVF        STORE,0     ;Place conversion in W
        BCF         STATUS,CARRY
        ADDLW       0xB5        ;Check for gain over 300
        BTFSC       STATUS,CARRY
        CALL        DOT6
        MOVF        STORE,0     ;Place conversion in W
        BCF         STATUS,CARRY
        ADDLW       9C          ;Check for gain over 400
        BTFSC       STATUS,CARRY
        CALL        DOT7
        MOVF        STORE,0     ;Place conversion in W
        BCF         STATUS,CARRY
        ADDLW       83          ;Check for gain over 500
        BTFSC       STATUS,CARRY
        CALL        DOT8
        MOVF        STORE,0     ;Place conversion in W
        BCF         STATUS,CARRY
        ADDLW       6A          ;Check for gain over 600
        BTFSC       STATUS,CARRY
        CALL        DOT9
        MOVF        STORE,0     ;Place conversion in W
        BCF         STATUS,CARRY
        ADDLW       38          ;Check for gain over 800
```

```
        BTFSC       STATUS,CARRY
        CALL        DOT10
        MOVF        DOTS,0
        MOVWF       PORTB
        MOVF        DOTS2,0
        MOVWF       PORTA
        CLRF        DOTS
        CLRF        DOTS2
        GOTO        LOOP
DOT1    MOVLW       01
        MOVWF       DOTS
        RETURN
DOT2    MOVLW       02
        MOVWF       DOTS
        RETURN
DOT3    MOVLW       04
        MOVWF       DOTS
        RETURN
DOT4    MOVLW       08
        MOVWF       DOTS
        RETURN
DOT5    MOVLW       10
        MOVWF       DOTS
        RETURN
DOT6    MOVLW       20
        MOVWF       DOTS
        RETURN
DOT7    MOVLW       40
        MOVWF       DOTS
        RETURN
DOT8    MOVLW       80
        MOVWF       DOTS
        RETURN
DOT9    CLRF        DOTS
        MOVLW       04
        MOVWF       DOTS2
        RETURN
DOT10   MOVLW       00
        MOVWF       DOTS2
        MOVLW       08
```

```
              MOVWF     PORTA
              MOVLW     50
              MOVWF     CNTR
DELAY         DECFSZ    CNTR,1
              GOTO      DELAY
              MOVLW     00
              MOVWF     PORTA
              MOVLW     50
              MOVWF     CNTR
DELAY2        DECFSZ    CNTR,1
              GOTO      DELAY2
              RETURN
END
```

Components For The Strength Meter (Figure 2.8)

Resistors (all 0.25 watt 5% carbon film)
R1   47k
R2   10k
R3 to R11   270R (9 off)
R12   3k9

Potentiometer
VR1   470k lin carbon rotary

Capacitors
C1   470n polyester
C2   220p polystyrene or ceramic plate

Semiconductors
IC1   16C71-04
D1 to D9   5mm Red panel LEDs (9 off)

Miscellaneous
LS1   Cased ceramic resonator
B1   4.5V (3 × AA size cells in holder)
S1   s.p.s.t. min toggle switch
Case, circuit board, materials for grip, battery connector (PP3 type), 18-pin DIL holder, control knob, wire solder, etc.

Reaction Timer

This simple reaction timing game has a two-digit display, which counts in (approximately) one hundredths of a second. It can therefore handle reaction times up to about 0.99 seconds (990 milliseconds). To start the game the reset button is pressed, and the display then reads '00'. After about 10 seconds the display starts to count in one hundredth second increments, and the player then has to press a second button as quickly as possible. The count halts as soon as the second button is pressed, and the display then shows the player's reaction time. In order to play again it is merely necessary to operate the reset button, which again resets the display to '00', and causes it to start counting again after about ten seconds. If the second pushbutton switch is not operated quickly enough, and the display cycles through '99', a software 'catch' detects the overrun and halts the count. The display is then set at '- -' to indicate that no valid time was produced. Once reset the unit will operate in the normal manner again.

Circuit Operation

The circuit diagram for the reaction tester is shown in Figure 2.9. To avoid the need for display multiplexing the circuit is based on a PIC 16C55 so that the two seven-segment LED displays can be driven from ports B and C. Port B drives the least significant digit and port C drives the most significant digit. Only the lower seven bits of each port are needed, and the most significant bit of each port is left unconnected. Resistor R17 and capacitor C1 are the timing components for the clock circuit, and their values have been chosen so that the display shows the reaction time in one hundredths of a second. Obviously a high degree of accuracy is not possible when using a simple C-R clock circuit, but a high degree of precision is not really needed in this application. It is comparative results that are of most interest. A unit of this type will clearly show the effect of even a small amount of alcohol on your reaction times. Lines RA1 and RA0 respectively monitor the reset switch (S1) and 'stop' switch (S2). Resistors R15 and R16 normally pull these inputs low, but operating one of the switches takes its input high.

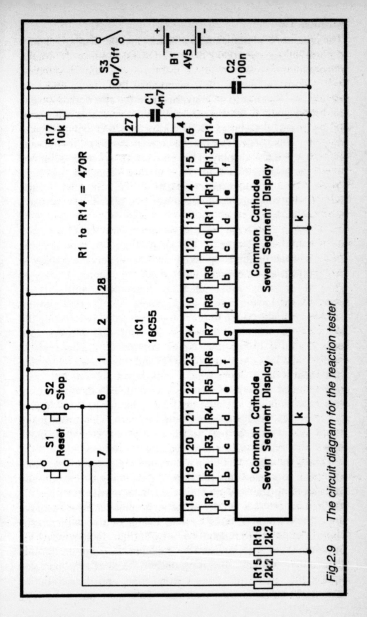

Fig.2.9   The circuit diagram for the reaction tester

Software

The program is complicated by the fact that the display is really a form of binary coded decimal (BCD) counter. A double conversion process is required if the count is kept in standard binary form, as it must be converted to BCD form, and then each BCD digit has to be converted into the appropriate seven-bit binary code to drive the display. Where possible it is easier if the count is taken in BCD form, and then only a single conversion is needed in order to convert the count into seven-bit codes for the display. This conversion is easily achieved using the standard look-up table method. The low and high nibbles of the count are respectively kept in LNIBL and HNIBL, but obviously only the lower four bits of these actually carry valid data.

The first part of the program sets up ports B and C as output ports, and then calls the 'STOP' subroutine. This routine loops until the reset button is operated, and then it sets the display to read '00'. It also clears both nibbles of the counter. A delay of several seconds must then be provided, and this is accomplished using a twin loop system. A delay of about ten seconds is long enough to prevent players from anticipating the start of the count, but is not so long that players lose concentration before the count commences. The register labelled CNTR is loaded with 0xFF, and this is used to provide a standard delay loop which ends when CNTR has been decremented to zero. However, a second loop then results in this process being repeated until the value of 30 (hex) loaded into CNTR2 has been decremented to zero. This gives many thousands of loops in total, and despite the relatively high clock frequency a delay of about 10 seconds is produced.

Once the delay has been completed the program goes into the main loop, and this provides the counting action. Simply incrementing the low nibble on each loop will not give the desired action, as it will leave the high nibble at zero! Also, the low nibble would be taken beyond a value of nine, which is the highest permissible number for a BCD digit. Incrementing the high nibble is accomplished by XORing the value in the low nibble with 0A (hex). If this produces a result of zero the value in the low nibble has gone beyond nine, and the subroutine called 'PLUSH' is then executed. This increments the high nibble and clears the low nibble. The same method of testing is used to check the high nibble. If this goes beyond a value of nine the counter has overflowed, and a warning must be shown on the display. This warning is provided by the subroutine labelled 'OVER', which switches on the 'g' (middle) segments of the two seven segment displays, and then calls the STOP subroutine. Once the latter has been completed the program is branched back into the main loop by a GOTO instruction, and a fresh count is started in the normal fashion.

```
;************************************************
;Two Digit Counter Program
;Least Significant Digit on RB0 to RB6
;Most Significant Digit on RC0 to RC6
;************************************************
;
STATUS   EQU      03
Z        EQU      02
C        EQU      0
LNIBL    EQU      0A
HNIBL    EQU      0B
CNTR     EQU      0E
CNTR2    EQU      0F
STORE    EQU      0C
PORTA    EQU      05
PORTB    EQU      06
PORTC    EQU      07
PC       EQU      02
OVER9    EQU      0D
         CLRW
         TRIS     06          ;Set Port B as outputs
         TRIS     07          ;Set Port C as outputs
         CALL     STOP
LOOP     MOVF     LNIBL,W
         BCF      STATUS,Z
         XORLW    0A
         BTFSC    STATUS,Z    ;Check if low nibble reached 10
         CALL     PLUSH       ;Zero and INC high nibble if it is
         MOVF     LNIBL,W
         CALL     TABLE
```

99

	MOVWF	PORTB	;Output data to port B
MOVF	HNIBL,W		
	BCF	STATUS,Z	
	XORLW	0A	
	BTFSC	STATUS,Z	;Check if high nibble reached 10
	GOTO	OVER	;Branch if it has
	MOVF	HNIBL,W	
	CALL	TABLE	;Load W with display data
	MOVWF	PORTC	;Output data to Port C
	INCF	LNIBL,1	;Increment counter
	BTFSC	PORTA,0	
	CALL	STOP	;Branch to STOP if stop button pressed
	GOTO	LOOP	
OVER	MOVLW	40	
	MOVWF	PORTB	
	MOVWF	PORTC	
	GOTO	OVER2	
PLUSH	INCF	HNIBL	
	CLRF	LNIBL	
	RETLW	00	
STOP	BTFSS	PORTA,1	
	GOTO	STOP	;Wait for reset button to be pressed
	MOVLW	3F	
	MOVWF	PORTB	
	MOVWF	PORTC	;Set display at '00'
	CLRF	LNIBL	
	CLRF	HNIBL	;Clear both nibbles of counter
	MOVLW	0xFF	
	MOVWF	CNTR	
	MOVLW	30	
	MOVWF	CNTR2	
DELAY	DECFSZ	CNTR,1	
	GOTO	DELAY	
	DECFSZ	CNTR2,1	
	GOTO	DELAY	;Wait before starting new timing run
	RETLW 00		
TABLE	ADDWF	PC,1	

100

```
RETLW    3F
RETLW    06
RETLW    5B
RETLW    4F
RETLW    66
RETLW    6D
RETLW    7D
RETLW    07
RETLW    7F
RETLW    6F
END
```

Components For Reaction Timer (Figure 2.9)

Resistors (all 0.25 watt 5% carbon film)
R1 to R14   470R (14 off)
R15,16   2k2 (2 off)
R17   10k

Capacitors
C1   4n7 polyester
C2   100n ceramic

Semiconductors
IC1   PIC 16C55
Displays   Common cathode 7-segment LED display
                (2 off)

Miscellaneous
S1,2   Push-to-make switch (2 off)
S3   s.p.s.t. min toggle switch
B1   4V5 (3 × AA size cells in holder)
Case, circuit board, battery connector (PP3 type), 28-pin DIL
holder, wire, solder, etc.

Christmas Tree Lights Controller – 1

This perennial subject never seems to lose its popularity, and no
excuses are made for including two simple Christmas tree
lights controllers in this book. The first drives eight LEDs, and

these produce patterns that are controlled by eight switches. The basic idea is that the user uses the switches to produce an initial on/off pattern on the LEDs. The software then uses rotate instructions to 'move' the pattern around the line of LEDs. Two operating modes are available, and the first of these simply right shifts the display seven times, and then goes back to the beginning and repeats the process. The second mode starts in the same way, but having right shifted the LEDs seven times it then left shifts them seven times. This process is then repeated indefinitely. The action of the display is complicated slightly by the fact that the rotate instructions rotate the data through the carry/borrow flag. Consequently, the display does not always operate in quite the way one might expect. This is not necessarily a drawback though, and there is something to be said for a display that is slightly enigmatic. The lack of predictability tends to hold the interest of onlookers for longer. Commercially produced lights controllers often seem to produce slightly asymmetrical results that give the display some added interest. For those who prefer a more logical approach to things a lights controller which does things 'by the book' is described in the final section of this chapter.

Circuit Operation

The full circuit diagram for the programmable lights controller appears in Figure 2.10. On the input side of the PIC 16C55 microcontroller there are eight switches plus a pull-up resistor for each input line. Therefore, an input line is taken low when its switch is closed or high when the switch is open. The switches are read by port B. There is a ninth switch which is read by line RA0, and this one has pull-down resistor R18. This switch controls the operating mode of the unit. S1 is closed if normal operation is required, or opened if the backward and forwards effect is preferred. The eight LEDs are driven from port C via current limiting resistors R10 to R17. A drive current of about six to seven milliamps is used, which represents about the maximum that the processor chip can realistically handle. It is advisable to use high brightness or even ultra-bright LEDs so that good results are produced despite the fairly low drive current. Although red LEDs are specified for D1 to D8, these can obviously be LEDs of any desired colours.

102

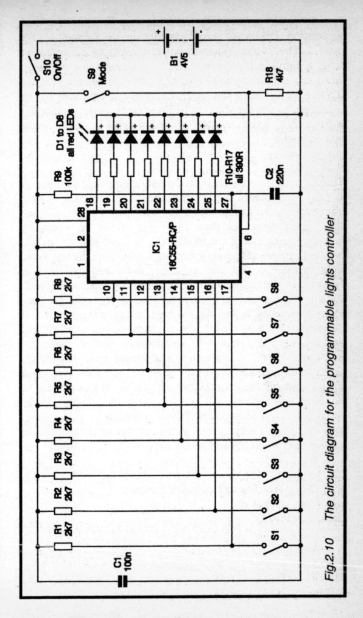

Fig.2.10   The circuit diagram for the programmable lights controller

103

A C-R clock gives more than adequate stability for this application. The timing components for the clock circuit are R9 and C2. This is an application where there is no advantage in using a high clock frequency and timing loops to slow things down to a suitable degree. Therefore, high values are used for R9 and C2 so that a low clock frequency is obtained. If you would prefer the speed of the LEDs to be variable, replace R9 with a 22k fixed resistor in series with a 220k linear potentiometer.

Software

The program first sets port C as an output type, and then port B is read. The binary pattern read from the switches is then transferred to the LEDs on port C. Next a series of seven rotate right instructions are performed, with three no operation instructions after each one to slow things down slightly. In fact only a single no operation instruction is used after the last rotate right instruction, but the additional delay required here is provided by the simple routine that checks the state of the mode switch. If the switch is closed and RA0 is high, the program loops back to the beginning and provides normal operation. If the mode switch is closed, the program moves onwards and performs seven rotate left instructions. Again, these are interspersed with no operation instructions that slow things down to the required degree. Once these have been performed the program returns to the beginning, reads port B again, and so on. Note that the unit will not respond to any changes in the settings of S1 to S8 until a new cycle is commenced. It is worth experimenting a little with various settings of these switches (and mode switch S9) to find the best effects.

```
;************************************************
;Christmas Tree Lights Controller Program
;Switches on Port B
;LEDs on Port C
;************************************************
;
PORTA      EQU        05
PORTB      EQU        06
PORTC      EQU        07
```

```
        CLRW
        TRIS    07          ;Set Port C as outputs
MAIN    MOVF    PORTB,0     ;Read port B
        MOVWF   PORTC       ;Set initial pattern on lights
        NOP
        NOP
        NOP
        RRF     PORTC
        NOP
        NOP
        NOP
        RRF     PORTC
        NOP
        NOP
        NOP
        RRF     PORTC
        NOP
        NOP
        NOP
        RRF     PORTC
        NOP
        NOP
        NOP
        RRF     PORTC
        NOP
        NOP
        NOP
        RRF     PORTC
        NOP
        NOP
        NOP
        RRF     PORTC
        NOP
        BTFSC   PORTA,0
        GOTO    MAIN
        RLF     PORTC
        NOP
        NOP
        NOP
        RLF     PORTC
```

```
        NOP
        NOP
        NOP
        RLF     PORTC
        NOP
        NOP
        NOP
        RLF     PORTC
        NOP
        NOP
        NOP
        RLF     PORTC
        NOP
        NOP
        NOP
        RLF     PORTC
        NOP
        NOP
        NOP
        RLF     PORTC
        NOP
        NOP
        NOP
        GOTO    MAIN
;
        END
```

Components for Christmas Tree Lights Controller – 1
(Figure 2.10)

Resistors (all 0.25 watt 5% carbon film)
R1 to R8	2k7 (8 off)
R9	100k
R10 to R17	390R (8 off)
R18	4k7

Capacitors
C1	100n ceramic
C2	220n polyester

Semiconductors
IC1   16C55-RC/P
D1 to D8   High brightness red LED (8 off)

Miscellaneous
B1   4V5 (3 × AA size cells in holder)
S1 to S10   s.p.s.t. min toggle (10 off)
Case, circuit board, 28-pin DIL holder, battery connector (PP3 type) wire, solder, etc.

Christmas Tree Lights Controller – 2

This lights controller is more simple than the one described previously in that it only goes through a preset routine, and it does not allow the user to control the lights in any way. Also, the routine performed is more conventional. The display consists of 12 LEDs, and initially these all light up. Then only every other LED is switched on, followed by all 12 LEDs switching states (i.e. those that were on switch off, and those that were off switch on). This alternating of the LEDs is repeated until ten on/off cycles have been completed. Basically the same process is then carried out again, but with the LEDs in groups of two, then three, four, and six. The LEDs are then switched off, after which they are all switched on again and the entire process is repeated indefinitely.

Figure 2.11 shows the circuit diagram for the simple lights controller. This consists of little more than the PIC 16C84 processor, the LEDs, and their current limiting resistors. D1 to D8 are driven from port B, and D9 to D12 are driven from port A. The clock circuit is a simple C-R type having R13 and C2 as the timing components. If a variable speed control is required, replace R13 with a 220k linear potentiometer in series with a 22k fixed resistor.

Software

The initial part of the program sets ports A and B as output types, and all 12 lines are then set high so that all the LEDs are switched on. A subroutine that provides a delay is then called, after which the odd numbered LEDs are switched off but the even numbered LEDs are left switched on. The delay

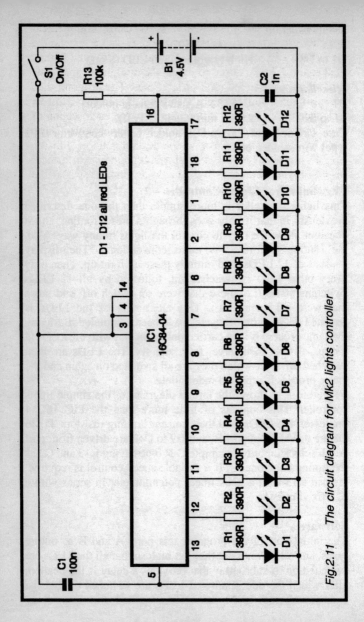

Fig.2.11   The circuit diagram for Mk2 lights controller

subroutine is then called again. Next using complement instructions to invert the port A and port B data registers, the states of the LEDs are reversed. The delay subroutine is then called again. A loop is used to repeat the blinking of the lights so that it is performed a total of ten times. The program then performs similar loops which flash the LEDs in twos, threes, fours, and sixes. The only differences between each section of the program are the values written to the output ports. These values have to be chosen to give the desired patterns. Finally, the LEDs are switched off, the delay subroutine is performed, and the program branches back to the beginning so that the entire routine is repeated indefinitely.

```
;************************************************
;Christmas Lights – 2 Program
;************************************************
;
STATUS      EQU       03
PORTA       EQU       05
PORTB       EQU       06
ADIR        EQU       05
BDIR        EQU       06
CNTR        EQU       0C
CNTR2       EQU       0D
            BSF       STATUS,5       ;Select page 1
            MOVLW     0xF0
            MOVWF     ADIR           ;Set Port A as outputs
            CLRW
            MOVWF     BDIR           ;Set port B as outputs
            BCF       STATUS,5       ;Select page 0
START       MOVLW     0F
            MOVWF     PORTA          ;Set port A high
            MOVLW     0xFF
            MOVWF     PORTB          ;Set port B high
            CALL      DELAY
            MOVLW     0A
            MOVWF     CNTR2
LOOP1       MOVLW     05
            MOVWF     PORTA          ;Write 0101 to port A
            MOVLW     55
```

```
              MOVWF     PORTB        ;Write 01010101 to port A
              CALL      DELAY
              COMF      PORTA,1
              COMF      PORTB,1      ;Invert ons and offs
              CALL      DELAY
              DECFSZ    CNTR2,1
              GOTO      LOOP1
              MOVLW     0A
              MOVWF     CNTR2
LOOP2         MOVLW     03
              MOVWF     PORTA        ;Write 0011 to port A
              MOVLW     33
              MOVWF     PORTB        ;Write 00110011 to port B
              CALL      DELAY
              COMF      PORTA,1
              COMF      PORTB,1      ;Invert ons and offs
              CALL      DELAY
              DECFSZ    CNTR2,1
              GOTO      LOOP2
              MOVLW     0A
              MOVWF     CNTR2
LOOP3         MOVLW     07
              MOVWF     PORTA        ;Write 0011 to port A
              MOVLW     1C
              MOVWF     PORTB        ;Write 00011100 to port B
              CALL      DELAY
              COMF      PORTA,1
              COMF      PORTB,1      ;Invert ons and offs
              CALL      DELAY
              DECFSZ    CNTR2,1
              GOTO      LOOP3
              MOVLW     0A
              MOVWF     CNTR2
LOOP4         MOVLW     0
              MOVWF     PORTA        ;Write 0000 to port A
              MOVLW     0F
              MOVWF     PORTB        ;Write 00001111 to port B
              CALL      DELAY
              COMF      PORTA,1
              COMF      PORTB,1      ;Invert ons and offs
```

110

```
         CALL      DELAY
         DECFSZ    CNTR2,1
         GOTO      LOOP4
         MOVLW     0A
         MOVWF     CNTR2
LOOP5    MOVLW     0F
         MOVWF     PORTA      ;Write 1111 to port A
         MOVLW     03
         MOVWF     PORTB      ;Write 00000011 to port B
         CALL      DELAY
         COMF      PORTA,1
         COMF      PORTB,1    ;Invert ons and offs
         CALL      DELAY
         DECFSZ    CNTR2,1
         GOTO      LOOP5
         CLRF      PORTA
         CLRF      PORTB      ;Switch off LEDs
         CALL      DELAY
         GOTO      START      ;Loop indefinitely
;
DELAY    MOVLW     0xFF
         MOVWF     CNTR
DELAY1   DECFSZ    CNTR,1
         GOTO      DELAY1
         RETURN
;
         END
```

Components for Christmas Tree Lights Controller – 2 (Figure 2.11)

Resistors (all 0.25 watt 5% carbon film)
R1 to R12   390R (12 off)
R13   100k

Capacitors
C1   100n ceramic
C2   1n polyester

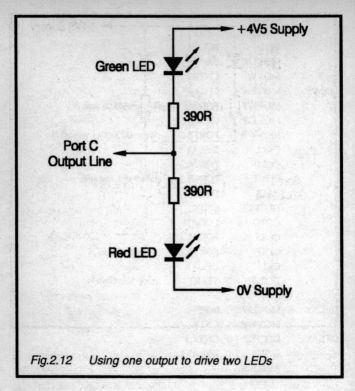

Fig.2.12   Using one output to drive two LEDs

Semiconductors

IC1	16C84-04
D1 to D12	Red LEDs (12 off)

Miscellaneous

S1	s.p.s.t. min toggle switch
B1	4V5 ($3 \times$ AA size cells in holder)

Case, circuit board, 18-pin DIL holder, battery connector (PP3 type), wire, solder, etc.

Improved Displays

A simple way of improving the displays of either lights controller is to simply add more LEDs. The easiest way of

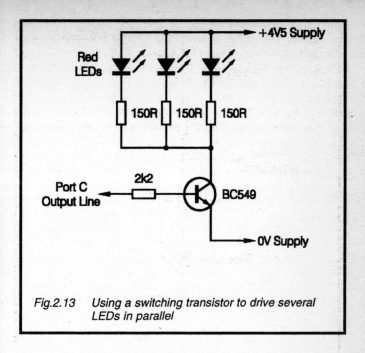

*Fig.2.13   Using a switching transistor to drive several
            LEDs in parallel*

achieving this is to use the complementary method shown in
Figure 2.12, where each output of the PIC microcontroller
drives two LEDs. However, things are arranged so that the
lower LED is switched on when the output is high, and the
upper LED is turned on when the output is low. If one green
LED and one red type are used, with the two components
mounted side-by-side, the effect obtained is that of a single
light which changes colour when the output changes state.

The circuit of Figure 2.13 enables several LEDs to be
driven in unison from each output, and also enables a higher
LED current to be used (a little under 20 milliamps). Although
three LEDs are shown in Figure 2.13, anything up to five LEDs
connected in parallel can be used. With a sixth LED used it is
likely that the collector current of the BC549 transistor might
exceed its maximum permissible figure of 100 milliamps.
Individual current limiting resistors are used for the LEDs to
ensure even illumination, and this also ensures that the circuit

will work properly if LEDs of different colours are used. Remember that using more LEDs will increase the current consumption of the circuit. Driving three lights from 12 outputs for example would give a current consumption of around 700 milliamps with all the LEDs switched on. A high capacity battery such as three 'high power' D size cells would be needed to provide this. Alternatively, either of the lights controller circuits can be powered from a five-volt mains power supply of adequate current rating.

Chapter 3

MISCELLANEOUS PROJECTS

Stereo VU Meter

The use of the PIC 16C71 as a bargraph driver was covered previously, but this project takes things a stage further by using the 16C71 in a stereo VU meter where it drives a twin eight-LED bargraph display. With two input/output lines used as analogue inputs there are just ten lines left for use as digital outputs. These are more than adequate to drive the sixteen LEDs of the display provided multiplexing is used. The basic multiplexing technique is to first take a reading on one channel and activate the display for that channel. Then a reading is taken on channel two and the result is displayed on the appropriate section of the display, but the channel one display is switched off. Next a reading is taken on channel one and the result is displayed, but the channel two display is switched off. This process is repeated indefinitely, with the two sections of the display being activated alternately. If the multiplexing operates at a low speed the strobing of the display is very obvious, and neither section of the display is easily read. However, if the displays are strobed at more than about 25 hertz the switching action becomes imperceptible, and both sections of the display appear to be switched on simultaneously and continuously.

The circuit consists basically of a twin bargraph preceded by two precision rectifiers and smoothing circuits (one to process each stereo channel). The rectifier and smoothing circuits produce a D.C. output level that is proportional to the peak amplitude of the input signal. There is potentially a slight advantage in using full-wave rectification because the input signal may not always be completely symmetrical, but for the sake of simplicity half-wave rectification is used in this design. The smoothing circuit must have a brief attack time and a much longer decay period. This ensures that any transient signals will produce a clear indication on the display and will not be overlooked. VU meters in professional audio equipment operate with standard attack and decay times of

115

0.5 milliseconds and 1 second respectively, and this circuit (more or less) conforms to this standard.

The eight-bit resolution of the analogue to digital converter in the PIC 16C71 enables a maximum dynamic range of about 48dB to be accommodated, but this is rather more than is normally required from a VU meter. The eight LEDs in this design operate at levels of –30, –20, –10, –6, –3, 0, +3, and +6dB, giving a 36dB dynamic range. However, by using the appropriate values in the program it is possible to use virtually any required levels that fall within the dynamic range of the circuit. At maximum sensitivity an input level of about 500 millivolts r.m.s. is needed to activate the +6dB LED. This should be adequate for most purposes, but if necessary the sensitivity can be boosted somewhat.

Circuit Operation
Figure 3.1 shows the circuit diagram for the two rectifier and smoothing circuits. As these are identical we will only consider operation of the one based on IC1. A simple diode rectifier is unsuitable for this application due to the pronounced non-linearity of semiconductor diodes. An active 'precision' rectifier therefore has to be used. IC1 operates as a non-inverting amplifier and D2 provides the rectification. D1 is included in the negative feedback network of IC1, and it introduces non-linear feedback that distorts the output signal. The point of this is that the distortion on the output signal from IC1 is the opposite of the distortion that occurs through D2. The forward voltage drop through D2 is therefore counteracted by an almost identical boost in the output voltage from IC1. An accurately half-wave rectified signal is therefore supplied to the smoothing circuit comprised by R4 and C2. The positive D.C. voltage generated across the smoothing circuit is coupled to the appropriate analogue input of the PIC processor via protection resistor R5.

Note that the device used for IC1 and IC2 must be one that can operate in single supply D.C. circuits. Most operational amplifiers will not operate properly in this circuit. Also note that the CA3140E specified for IC1 and IC2, like the PIC processor, is a static sensitive device. The usual anti-static handling precautions are therefore required for the three DIL

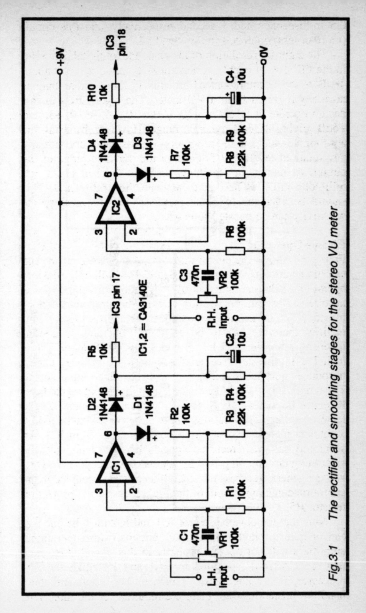

Fig.3.1   The rectifier and smoothing stages for the stereo VU meter.

117

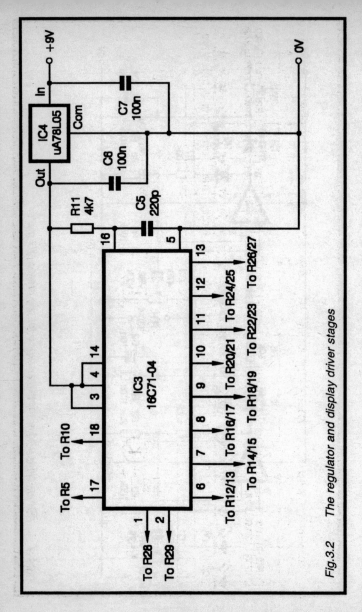

Fig.3.2   The regulator and display driver stages

118

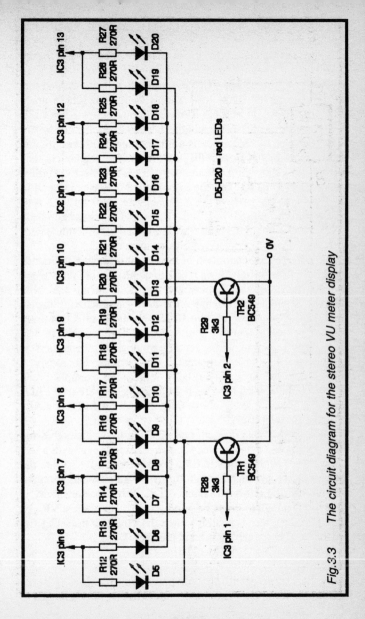

Fig.3.3   The circuit diagram for the stereo VU meter display

119

integrated circuits, but not for voltage regulator IC4 which is a bipolar device.

The circuit diagram for the display driver appears in Figure 3.2, while the circuit for the display itself is shown in Figure 3.3. The PIC processor (IC3) requires a 5-volt supply, and this is derived from the main 9-volt supply using monolithic voltage regulator IC4. R11 and C5 form the timing network for IC3's internal C-R clock circuit, and this is another application where the precise clock frequency is not important. However, it must be high enough to prevent display flicker. The display consists of pairs of LEDs, with odd numbered LEDs connected to the 0 volt supply via TR1, and the even number LEDs connected to the 0-volt rail by way of TR2. To activate (say) D12 pin 9 of IC3 would be placed high and TR2 would be switched on by taking IC3 pin 2 high. With the appropriate set of output states it is possible to activate any LED, or none of them.

The current consumption of the circuit is about 6 milliamps with no LEDs switched on, rising to about 16 milliamps when both sections of the display are active. Although the LED current is about 10 milliamps, the use of multiplexing means that this is split between two LEDs, giving an effective drive current of only about 5 milliamps. It is advisable to use reasonably efficient LEDs so that good display brightness is produced despite the modest LED current. Obviously a multicolour display can be used if desired. For example, green LEDs could be used for threshold levels below 0dB, red LEDs could be used for levels above 0dB, and yellow LEDs could be utilized for 0dB itself.

The unit is easy to calibrate, and the basic method is the same for both channels. Feed the two stereo inputs with a test tone that is at the required 0dB level. Adjust VR1 so that the sensitivity is just high enough to give a 0dB indication on the display for the left-hand channel (i.e. so that the sensitivity is just high enough to cause D15 to light up). Then adjust VR2 so that the sensitivity is just high enough to light up the 0dB LED in the display for the right-hand channel (D16).

Software
On the face of it the display multiplexing is very straightforward, but in practice it has to be carefully arranged in

order to avoid a 'ghost' image of one display appearing on the other section of the display. When using a microcontroller to drive the display it is not always possible to simultaneously write new data to one section of the display and switch off the other section. This is not possible in this case as the display data is written to port B and the on/off switching is controlled from port A. Fresh data for the display can be written to port B, and then that section of the display can be switched on via port A, or the display can be switched on and then the data for it can be written to port B. Either way the data momentarily appears on the wrong section of the display and a 'ghost' image is produced. The way around this problem is to switch off the display completely prior to writing new data to port B, and then switch on the appropriate section of the display. The display is then blanked while fresh data is written to port B, and no 'ghosting' occurs. It is for this reason that the display switching must be controlled by separate outputs of port A, rather than just having a single line which is set high to activate one section of the display, or low to switch on the other section.

The program has obvious similarities with the programs used in previous projects that utilize a 'dot' mode bargraph. In this case two analogue inputs are required, together with two digital outputs, and a value of 02 is therefore written to the ADCON1 register. Port A still has to be set up with RA0/1 as inputs and RA2/3 as outputs using the data direction register for port B. The main loop is much the same as for a single bargraph, but the reading of the analogue to digital converter and processing of the result is carried out twice on each loop. First channel 0 of the converter is read and data is output to the first section of the display, and then channel 1 is read and data is output to the second section of the display. In this application the two bargraphs must have identical scaling, and the same threshold values are therefore used for both of them. However, the display driver section of the unit could be used in applications that require the bargraphs to be used in different functions with different scaling. It is just a matter of using suitable threshold values in each section of the main program loop.

```
;**************************************************
;Stereo Dot Mode Bargraph Program
;**************************************************
;
CARRY    EQU     00
DOTS     EQU     0E
STATUS   EQU     03
ADIR     EQU     05
BDIR     EQU     06
ADCON    EQU     08
PORTA    EQU     05
PORTB    EQU     06
ADRES    EQU     09
STORE    EQU     0C
         BSF     STATUS,5    ;Select page 1
         CLRW
         MOVWF   BDIR        ;Sets Port B as outputs
         MOVLW   0xF3
         MOVWF   ADIR        ;Sets RA2/3 as outputs
         MOVLW   02
         MOVWF   ADCON       ;Sets RA0/1 as A/D, RA2/3 as
                             ;digital
         BCF     STATUS,5    ;Select page 0
LOOP     MOVLW   0xC1
         MOVWF   ADCON       ;Select Ch0/Int clock
         BSF     ADCON,2     ;Start conversion
         NOP                 ;Wait
         MOVF    ADRES,0     ;Place conversion in W
         MOVWF   STORE       ;Place conversion in STORE
         BCF     STATUS,CARRY
         ADDLW   0xFD        ;Check for reading over -30dB
         BTFSC   STATUS,CARRY
         CALL    DOT1
         MOVF    STORE,0     ;Place conversion in W
         BCF     STATUS,CARRY
         ADDLW   0xF6        ;Check for reading over -20dB
         BTFSC   STATUS,CARRY
         CALL    DOT2
         MOVF    STORE,0     ;Place conversion in W
         BCF     STATUS,CARRY
```

122

```
ADDLW    0xE0          ;Check for reading over -10dB
BTFSC    STATUS,CARRY
CALL     DOT3
MOVF     STORE,0       ;Place conversion in W
BCF      STATUS,CARRY
ADDLW    0xCE          ;Check for reading over -6dB
BTFSC    STATUS,CARRY
CALL     DOT4
MOVF     STORE,0       ;Place conversion in W
BCF      STATUS,CARRY
ADDLW    0xB9          ;Check for reading over -3dB
BTFSC    STATUS,CARRY
CALL     DOT5
MOVF     STORE,0       ;Place conversion in W
BCF      STATUS,CARRY
ADDLW    9C            ;Check for reading over 0dB
BTFSC    STATUS,CARRY
CALL     DOT6
MOVF     STORE,0       ;Place conversion in W
BCF      STATUS,CARRY
ADDLW    73            ;Check for reading over +3dB
BTFSC    STATUS,CARRY
CALL     DOT7
MOVF     STORE,0       ;Place conversion in W
BCF      STATUS,CARRY
ADDLW    38            ;Check for reading over +6dB
BTFSC    STATUS,CARRY
CALL     DOT8
CLRF     PORTA         ;Switch off display
MOVF     DOTS,0
MOVWF    PORTB         ;Write data to display
BSF      PORTA,2       ;Switch on display
CLRF     DOTS          ;Clear DOTS register

;

MOVLW    0xC9
MOVWF    ADCON         ;Select Ch1/Int clock
BSF      ADCON,2       ;Start conversion
NOP                    ;Wait
MOVF     ADRES,0       ;Place conversion in W
MOVWF    STORE         ;Place conversion in STORE
```

```
BCF      STATUS,CARRY
ADDLW    0xFD          ;Check for reading over -30dB
BTFSC    STATUS,CARRY
CALL     DOT1
MOVF     STORE,0       ;Place conversion in W
BCF      STATUS,CARRY
ADDLW    0xF6          ;Check for reading over -20dB
BTFSC    STATUS,CARRY
CALL     DOT2
MOVF     STORE,0       ;Place conversion in W
BCF      STATUS,CARRY
ADDLW    0xE0          ;Check for reading over -10dB
BTFSC    STATUS,CARRY
CALL     DOT3
MOVF     STORE,0       ;Place conversion in W
BCF      STATUS,CARRY
ADDLW    0xCE          ;Check for reading over -6dB
BTFSC    STATUS,CARRY
CALL     DOT4
MOVF     STORE,0       ;Place conversion in W
BCF      STATUS,CARRY
ADDLW    0xB9          ;Check for reading over -3dB
BTFSC    STATUS,CARRY
CALL     DOT5
MOVF     STORE,0       ;Place conversion in W
BCF      STATUS,CARRY
ADDLW    9C            ;Check for reading over 0dB
BTFSC    STATUS,CARRY
CALL     DOT6
MOVF     STORE,0       ;Place conversion in W
BCF      STATUS,CARRY
ADDLW    73            ;Check for reading over +3dB
BTFSC    STATUS,CARRY
CALL     DOT7
MOVF     STORE,0       ;Place conversion in W
BCF      STATUS,CARRY
ADDLW    38            ;Check for reading over +6dB
BTFSC    STATUS,CARRY
CALL     DOT8
CLRF     PORTA         ;Switch off display
```

```
          MOVF      DOTS,0
          MOVWF     PORTB        ;Write data to display
          BSF       PORTA,3
          CLRF      DOTS         ;Clear DOTS register
          GOTO      LOOP
;
DOT1      MOVLW     01
          MOVWF     DOTS
          RETURN
DOT2      MOVLW     02
          MOVWF     DOTS
          RETURN
DOT3      MOVLW     04
          MOVWF     DOTS
          RETURN
DOT4      MOVLW     08
          MOVWF     DOTS
          RETURN
DOT5      MOVLW     10
          MOVWF     DOTS
          RETURN
DOT6      MOVLW     20
          MOVWF     DOTS
          RETURN
DOT7      MOVLW     40
          MOVWF     DOTS
          RETURN
DOT8      MOVLW     80
          MOVWF     DOTS
          RETURN
          END
```

Components for Stereo VU Meter (Figures 3.1, 3.2 and 3.3)

Resistors (all 0.25 watt 5% carbon film)
R1, R2, R4,
R6, R7, R9   100k (6 off)
R3, R8   22k (2 off)
R5, R10   10k (2 off)

R11	4k7
R12 to R27	270R (16 off)
R28, R29	3k3 (2 off)

Potentiometers
| VR1, VR2 | 100k min hor preset (2 off) |

Capacitors
C1, C3	470n polyester (2 off)
C2, C4	10µ 25V radial elect (2 off)
C5	220p ceramic plate or polystyrene
C6, C7	100n ceramic (2 off)

Semiconductors
IC1, IC2	CA3140E (2 off)
IC3	PIC 16C71-04
IC4	µA78L05 (+5V 100mA regulator)
D1, D2, D3, D4	1N4148 (4 off)
D5 to D20	High brightness panel LEDs (16 off)
TR1, TR2	BC549 (2 off)

Miscellaneous
Case, circuit board, 8-pin DIL holder (2 off), 18-pin DIL holder, wire, solder, etc.

Combination Lock – 1
Using a microcontroller it is possible to implement any normal form of combination lock. This lock has ten pushbutton switches marked '0' to '9', and the lock is opened by entering the correct four-digit number. The software is easily modified to produce a longer combination if preferred, but it is probably best to settle for a short combination that is easily remembered. Even with just a four-digit combination the odds against opening the lock by a lucky guess are 9999 to 1!

The circuit diagram for the combination lock appears in Figure 3.4. A PIC 16C84 is ideal for this application as it can simply be reprogrammed with a new combination if the existing one gets into the wrong hands. It is generally considered to be a good idea to change the combination from

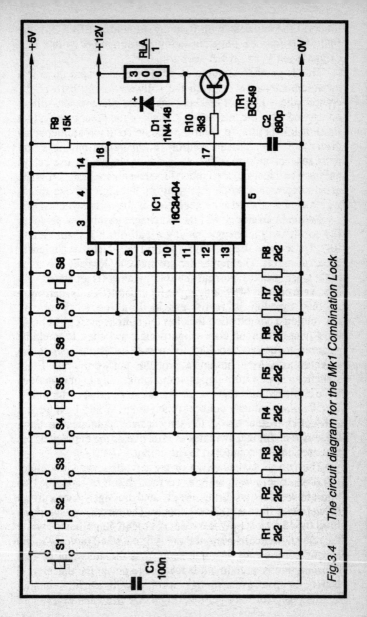

Fig.3.4   The circuit diagram for the Mk1 Combination Lock

127

time to time anyway. With its program held in EEPROM, the PIC 16C84 can be almost instantly reprogrammed with a new combination as and when necessary.

This is another example of a PIC project where there is a minimum of hardware, with the software taking care of the complexities. Resistor R9 and capacitor C2 are the timing components for the internal C-R clock of the processor. Output RA0 of IC1 is used to control a simple common emitter relay driver (TR1) which can control 12 volt relays having a coil resistance of around 300R. It is advisable not to use relays having a coil resistance of much less than about 200R. D1 is the usual suppression diode that removes the high voltage spikes which would otherwise be generated as the relay switched off.

On the input side of IC1 there are eight pushbutton switches (S1 to S8) with each one having a pull-down resistor (R1 to R8). These drive the eight lines of port B, which are obviously all set as inputs. The input lines are normally low and are taken high when one of the pushbutton switches is operated. No hardware contact 'de-bouncing' is incorporated in the hardware as this function is easily provided in the software. By convention a combination lock has ten buttons marked from '0' to '9', but this circuit only supports eight switches. It would be possible to utilize two lines of port A to permit two more switches to be used, but this is probably not worthwhile. Eight switches still permits a large number of four digit combinations to be used, and the other two switches can simply be 'dummies' which do not actually connect to anything. Would-be intruders will not know that two of the switches are 'dummies', making these two additional switches as effective as the eight switches that are actually connected to the circuit.

The current consumption of the circuit is very low under standby conditions, with a current drain of around two milliamps from the 5-volt supply and no significant current being drawn from the 12-volt supply. The current consumption from the 12-volt supply increases to around 40 milliamps while the relay is switched on, and there is also a small increase in the consumption on the five volt supply. As the quiescent current consumption is quite low it is feasible to power the unit from a battery supply, even though it may well be left running continuously for long periods. Eight AA size cells in a holder

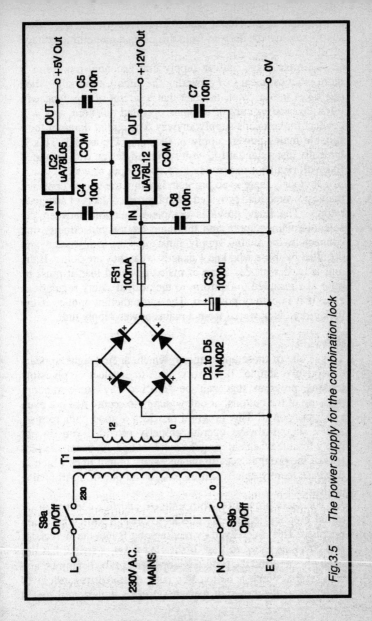

Fig. 3.5   The power supply for the combination lock

can be used to provide a main 12-volt supply, and the 5-volt supply can then be derived from this using a monolithic voltage regulator.

A simple mains power supply unit probably represents a more practical means of powering the circuit, especially when one takes into account the fact that a circuit of this type will often be used to control a mains operated solenoid, and will connect to the mains supply anyway. The circuit diagram for a suitable mains power supply is shown in Figure 3.5. This is basically just a standard 12-volt stabilised design with an added five-volt regulator to provide a +5 volt output as well.

Obviously there is no problem in using the unit to control a mains powered load provided the relay has contacts of adequate ratings. The relay provides complete isolation between the solenoid/mains supply and the main circuit, but circuits that connect to the mains supply must only be constructed and installed by those who know exactly what they are doing. If the unit is used with any form of mains powered load it must be built and installed to conform to the normal safety regulations even if it is battery powered. The same dictum applies if the lock circuit is powered from a mains power supply unit.

Software

This is one of those applications, which, at first sight, appears deceptively simple. It is very easy to produce a plausible looking program that can be 'cracked' by some random pressing of the buttons, or one which is so secure that not even you can open it! This program provides a good compromise, and it should always operate properly provided you do not badly fumble when entering the combination. As usual, the first part of the program sets up the necessary output lines which in this case merely entails setting RA0 as an output. RA0 is also set low initially.

The main program is then entered, and this consists of an initial loop that repeatedly checks to see if a switch has been operated. This is achieved by reading port B into the W register and checking the zero flag. If the flag is set, a switch has not been operated and the program loops back to the beginning and tries again. When a button has been operated, regardless of which one, the program branches to the subprogram called

CMB1. This checks to determine whether or not the first button in the combination has been pressed, and this is achieved by subtracting the appropriate number from the value read from port B, and testing to see if it produces a result of zero. The example values used in this program require S8, S7, S6, and S5 to be pressed (in that order) to activate the lock, but the values can obviously be changed to give any desired combination. This table shows the value used to test each of the eight pushbutton switches.

Switch	Value to Subtract (Dec)	Value to Subtract (Hex)
S1	128	80
S2	64	40
S3	32	20
S4	16	10
S5	8	08
S6	4	04
S7	2	02
S8	1	01

The program branches back to the main loop if the wrong button has been pressed. This ensures that there is a minimal chance of the lock being opened if someone simply presses the buttons at random. Each time an incorrect button is pressed things are moved back to 'square one', and the lock can only be operated by hitting the right four buttons, in sequence, with no other presses in between. If the right button is pressed the program loops until the button has been released. The program then branches back to the main program loop, but not to the very beginning. Instead it moves on a stage, and after a delay which provides contact de-bouncing the pushbutton switches are monitored once again. As before, the program loops until any switch or switches has been operated, and then it branches to a subprogram. However, it branches to a different subprogram (CMB2) which operates in much the same way as CMB1, but it tests for a different pushbutton switch.

Assuming the right switch has been pressed, the program waits until it is released again, and then returns to the main program loop again. Here a further de-bounce delay is provided, the pushbutton switches are monitored again, and so on. This general scheme of things continues until the correct four switches have been operated and released. The relay is then switched on, a delay is provided, and then the relay is switched off again. The delay holds the relay on for about one second or so, but a longer delay can obviously be used here if necessary. Finally, the program loops back to the beginning of the main loop and starts monitoring the pushbutton switches again.

```
;************************************************
;Combination Lock Program – 1
;************************************************
;
STATUS    EQU      03
Z         EQU      02
PORTA     EQU      05
PORTB     EQU      06
ADIR      EQU      05
CNTR      EQU      0C
CNTR2     EQU      0D
          BSF      STATUS,5      ;Select page 1
          MOVLW    0xFE
          MOVWF    ADIR          ;Set RA0 as output
          BCF      STATUS,5      ;Select page 0
          CLRF     PORTA         ;Set RA0 low initially
START     MOVF     PORTB,0
          BTFSS    STATUS,Z
          GOTO     CMB1
          GOTO     START         ;Loop until a button is pressed
START2    MOVLW    80
          MOVWF    CNTR
DELAY1    DECFSZ   CNTR,1
          GOTO     DELAY1        ;Provide de-bounce delay
LOOP5     MOVF     PORTB,0
          BTFSS    STATUS,Z
          GOTO     CMB2
          GOTO     LOOP5         ;Loop until a button is pressed
START3    MOVLW    80
          MOVWF    CNTR
DELAY2    DECFSZ   CNTR,1
```

132

	GOTO	DELAY2	;Provide de-bounce delay
LOOP6	MOVF	PORTB,0	
	BTFSS	STATUS,Z	
	GOTO	CMB3	
	GOTO	LOOP6	;Loop until a button is pressed
START4	MOVLW	80	
	MOVWF	CNTR	
DELAY3	DECFSZ	CNTR,1	
	GOTO	DELAY3	;Provide de-bounce delay
LOOP7	MOVF	PORTB,0	
	BTFSS	STATUS,Z	
	GOTO	CMB4	
	GOTO	LOOP7	;Loop until a button is pressed
START5	BSF	PORTA,0	;Switch on relay
	MOVLW	0xFF	
	MOVWF	CNTR	
	MOVLW	40	
	MOVWF	CNTR2	
DELAY4	DECFSZ	CNTR,1	
	GOTO	DELAY4	
	DECFSZ	CNTR2,1	
	GOTO	DELAY4	;Hold relay on for a while
	BCF	PORTA,0	;Switch off relay
	GOTO	START	;Loop back to start of main program
;			
CMB1	BCF	STATUS,Z	
	SUBLW	01	
	BTFSS	STATUS,Z	;Check for button 1 pressed
	GOTO	START	;Start again if it is not
LOOP1	MOVF	PORTB,0	
	BTFSC	STATUS,Z	
	GOTO	START2	
	GOTO	LOOP1	;Wait for button to be released
;			
CMB2	BCF	STATUS,Z	
	SUBLW	02	
	BTFSS	STATUS,Z	;Check for button 2 pressed
	GOTO	START	;Start again if it is not
LOOP2	MOVF	PORTB,0	

133

```
        BTFSC     STATUS,Z
        GOTO      START3
        GOTO      LOOP2       ;Wait for button to be released
;
CMB3    BCF       STATUS,Z
        SUBLW     04
        BTFSS     STATUS,Z    ;Check for button 3 pressed
        GOTO      START       ;Start again if it is not
LOOP3   MOVF      PORTB,0
        BTFSC     STATUS,Z
        GOTO      START4
        GOTO      LOOP3       ;Wait for button to be released
;
CMB4    BCF       STATUS,Z
        SUBLW     08
        BTFSS     STATUS,Z    ;Check for button 4 pressed
        GOTO      START       ;Start again if it is not
LOOP4   MOVF      PORTB,0
        BTFSC     STATUS,Z
        GOTO      START5
        GOTO      LOOP4       ;Wait for button to be released
END
```

Components For Combination Lock – 1 (Figures 3.4 and 3.5)

Resistors (all 0.25 watt 5% carbon film)
R1 to R8   2k2 (8 off)
R9   15k
R10   3k3

Capacitors
C1, C4, C5,
C6, C7   100n ceramic (5 off)
C2   680p polystyrene or ceramic plate
C3   1000µ 25V elect

Semiconductors
IC1   16C84-04
IC2   µA78L05 (+5V 100mA regulator)

134

IC3	µA78L12 (+12V 100mA regulator)
D1	1N4148
D2 to D5	1N4002 (4 off)
TR1	BC549

Miscellaneous

T1	Standard mains primary, 12 volt 200mA or more secondary
S1 to S8	Push-to-make switch (8 off)
S9	Rotary mains switch
FS1	100mA 20mm quick-blow
RLA/1	12 volt coil having a resistance of 200R or more, plus suitable contacts for the controlled equipment

Case, circuit board, control knob, 18-pin DIL holder, mains lead and plug, 20mm fuse holder, wire, solder, etc.

Note that two additional 'dummy' pushbutton switches will be needed if ten switches are needed in the keypad.

Combination Lock – 2

This combination lock uses exactly the same hardware as the lock described previously, but a different program converts the hardware into a slightly different form of lock. Rather than pressing four buttons in sequence, in order to open this lock it is necessary to press three buttons simultaneously, followed by another three buttons that must also be pressed together. The user has to remember two three-digit numbers, and get them in the right order, which should not be too difficult. Anyone trying to 'crack' the lock has a problem in that they stand no chance at all unless they know that two three-digit codes are required. Even if they do, the chances of opening the lock by sheer good fortune are extremely remote. In fact the odds are about a million to one against at each attempt! This type of combination lock is very easy to use, but provides excellent security.

The software works in a similar manner to the previous combination lock program. After the initial setting up of the ports, etc., the program monitors port B and loops until one or more of the pushbuttons have been pressed. The program then branches to CMB1 where a short delay is provided. This gives the user time to get all three switches closed before port B is read and the returned value is checked. This checking uses the standard method of subtraction and testing to see if the zero flag has been set. The value subtracted in this case is 0E (hex), which gives a result of zero only if S6 to S8 are pressed. Obviously this value can be changed to suit other switch combinations, and it is possible to make the program respond to anything from one to all eight switches. If the wrong value is detected the program goes back to the start of the main loop. Otherwise the program waits for the switches to be released and then it branches back to START2, where the pushbutton switches are monitored once again. The whole process is then repeated, but this time subprogram CMB2 checks that switches S1 to S3 have been pressed. Provided they have the program branches back into the main loop where the relay is switched on for a second or two before the main loop is restarted.

```
;************************************************
;Combination Lock Program – 2
;************************************************
;
STATUS    EQU     03
Z         EQU     02
PORTA     EQU     05
PORTB     EQU     06
ADIR      EQU     05
CNTR      EQU     0C
CNTR2     EQU     0D
          BSF     STATUS,5    ;Select page 1
          MOVLW   0xFE
          MOVWF   ADIR        ;Set RA0 as output
          BCF     STATUS,5    ;Select page 0
          CLRF    PORTA       ;Set RA0 low initially
START     MOVF    PORTB,0
          BTFSS   STATUS,Z
          GOTO    CMB1
          GOTO    START       ;Loop until a button is pressed
START2    MOVLW   80
          MOVWF   CNTR
DELAY1    DECFSZ  CNTR,1
```

136

	GOTO	DELAY1	;Provide de-bounce delay
LOOP3	MOVF	PORTB,0	
	BTFSS	STATUS,Z	
	GOTO	CMB2	
	GOTO	LOOP3	;Loop until a button is pressed
RELAY	BSF	PORTA,0	;Switch on relay
	MOVLW	0xFF	
	MOVWF	CNTR	
	MOVLW	40	
	MOVWF	CNTR2	
DELAY2	DECFSZ	CNTR,1	
	GOTO	DELAY2	
	DECFSZ	CNTR2,1	
	GOTO	DELAY2	;Hold relay on for a while
	BCF	PORTA,0	;Switch off relay
	GOTO	START	;Loop back to start of main program

;

CMB1	MOVLW	80	
	MOVWF	CNTR	
DELAY3	DECFSZ	CNTR,1	
	GOTO	DELAY3	;Wait for switches to settle
	MOVF	PORTB,0	
	BCF	STATUS,Z	
	SUBLW	07	
	BTFSS	STATUS,Z	;Check for buttons 6-7-8 pressed
	GOTO	START	;Start again if it is not
LOOP1	MOVF	PORTB,0	
	BTFSC	STATUS,Z	
	GOTO	START2	
	GOTO	LOOP1	;Wait for buttons to be released

;

CMB2	MOVLW	80	
	MOVWF	CNTR	
DELAY4	DECFSZ	CNTR,1	
	GOTO	DELAY4	;Wait for switches to settle
	MOVF	PORTB,0	
	BCF	STATUS,Z	
	SUBLW	0xE0	
	BTFSS	STATUS,Z	;Check for buttons 1-2-3 pressed

137

```
          GOTO      START       ;Start again if it is not
LOOP2     MOVF      PORTB,0
          BTFSC     STATUS,Z
          GOTO      RELAY
          GOTO      LOOP2       ;Wait for buttons to be released
          END
```

Two-Digit Voltmeter

This simple digital voltmeter has two-digit resolution and
covers a range of 0 to 9.9 volts. It utilizes the built-in analogue
to digital converter of a PIC 16C71, and uses the chip's digital
outputs to drive a two-digit seven-segment LED display. As
only ten digital lines are available it is necessary to resort to
multiplexing so that the fourteen segments of the display can be
driven. The basic full scale input voltage of the 16C71 is about
1.94 volts, but an attenuator reduces the sensitivity of the
circuit as a whole to 9.9 volts, which ties in nicely with the '00'
to '99' range of the display. Alternatively, a D.C. amplifier can
be added at the input of the circuit to boost its sensitivity to 0.99
volts (see below). Note that the operational amplifier used in
this circuit must be a type intended for single supply D.C.
operation and that few devices will work properly in place of
the CA3140E specified for IC3. Devices such as the µA741C,
TIL071CP, and LF351N will certainly not work in this circuit.

The circuit diagram for the voltmeter appears in Figures 3.6
and 3.7. R1, R2, and VR1 form the attenuator at the input. The
latter is adjusted to give the correct full-scale sensitivity. The
input resistance of the voltmeter is quite high at well over one
megohm. In terms of kilohms per volt this equates to around
110k per volt. Resistor R3 and capacitor C1 are the timing
components for the C-R clock circuit. In order to obtain good
accuracy and consistent results the circuit must be powered
from a well stabilised five-volt supply. This is derived from a
non-regulated nine-volt supply (e.g. a battery) by way of
monolithic voltage regulator IC2. Of course, the circuit can be
powered from any stable five-volt supply that can provide
currents of up to about 50 milliamps or so. The circuit diagram
for the D.C. amplifier previously mentioned is shown in Figure
3.8.

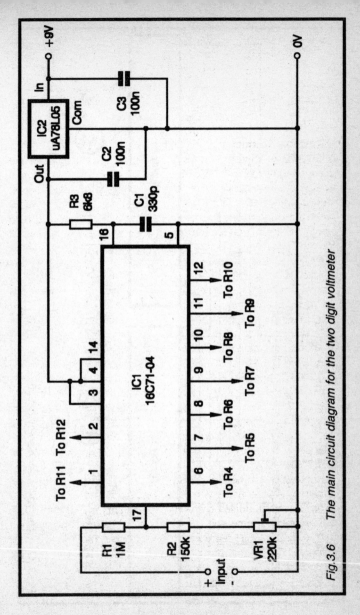

Fig. 3.6   The main circuit diagram for the two digit voltmeter

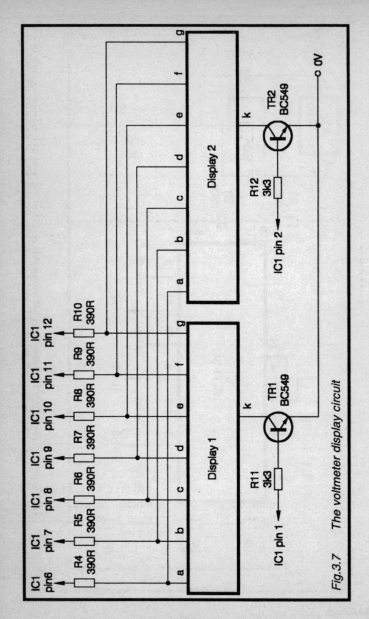

Fig.3.7   The voltmeter display circuit

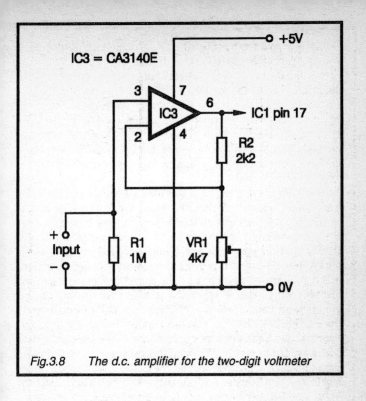

Fig.3.8   The d.c. amplifier for the two-digit voltmeter

Display multiplexing has been covered in previously, and it will not be described in detail again here. Segments 'a' to 'g' of the displays are driven from the seven least significant lines of port B via current limiting resistors R4 to R10. The two displays are controlled from RA2 and RA3 using switching transistors TR1 and TR2. If the 9.9 volt version of the circuit is constructed it would obviously be preferable to power the decimal point segment of the appropriate seven segment display. Virtually all modern displays have a right hand decimal point, and it is therefore the decimal point of display one that must be activated. Simply wire a 390R resistor between its decimal point terminal and the +5 volt supply.

Software

On the face of it there is no difficulty in reading eight-bit binary values from the analogue to digital converter, and then converting the two four-bit nibbles into seven bit codes to drive the displays using the look-up table method. In practice there is a major complication in that the values read from the converter are in standard binary form, but the display requires its raw data in binary coded decimal (BCD) form. There are various methods of converting from pure binary to BCD, including mathematical means, a counting/looping system, and the lookup table method.

After some experiments it was the lookup table method that was finally adopted. It has the disadvantage of requiring a relatively large amount of ROM, but the one hundred or so bytes required only represents about 10 percent of the 16C71's ROM, so this is not really a problem. A big advantage of using a lookup table is that it provides an almost instant conversion, making it unnecessary to merge the conversion process into the display multiplexing. It is possible to take a conversion, change the eight-bit value from the converter into BCD form, convert the BCD nibbles into the seven-bit codes for the displays, and then switch on the displays one at a time while the appropriate codes are fed to port B. Provided this process is repeated more than about 25 times per second the display will appear to be stable and continuous. Both displays will be switched off for only a small percentage of each display cycle, giving no problems with poor display brightness.

As usual, the initial part of the program sets up the required output lines, and in this case also sets RA0 and RA1 as analogue inputs. The input signal is applied to RA0, and is read as channel 0 of the converter. Input RA1 is left unused. The converter is set to use the internal clock circuit. A conversion is started at the beginning of the main program loop, and after a short delay the converter is read and the returned value is stored in STORE. Next a check is made to determine whether or not the returned value is too high to be displayed (i.e. whether or not it is at a decimal value of more than 99, or 63 in hexadecimal). This is achieved by subtracting 63 (hex) from the returned value and testing the state of the carry/borrow flag in the status register. If the value is too high, the program branches to the subprogram 'OVERLD', which writes a value of 40 (hex) to port B. The first digit is then switched on, and after a delay it is switched off again. After this process has been repeated for the second digit the program returns to the beginning of the main program loop and a new conversion is started. The value of 40 written to port B results in '- -' being displayed incidentally, which makes it clear that an out of range reading has been obtained.

If the returned value is in-range, the program calls the binary to BCD lookup table, and the returned BCD value is stored in both LNIBL (low nibble) and HNIBL (high nibble). Four rotate right instructions are used to move the upper nibble of HNIBL into the low nibble position. Some bitwise ANDing on both LNIBL and HNIBL then clears the upper four bits so that the required four bit values remain. These can then be used with a second lookup table (TABLE2) to provide the conversion to seven-bit codes that can drive the seven-segment displays. These conversions are provided immediately prior to outputting the data to port B. Once new data has been written to port B the appropriate digit is switched on, and then turned off again after a short delay. Once both digits have been displayed, the program returns to the beginning of the main loop and a new conversion/display cycle is commenced. The program loops indefinitely, taking a continuous series of readings and updating the display about 30 times per second.

```
;************************************************
;Two-digit Voltmeter Program
;************************************************
;
STATUS    EQU    03
CARRY     EQU    00
ADIR      EQU    05
BDIR      EQU    06
ADCON     EQU    08
PORTA     EQU    05
PORTB     EQU    06
ADRES     EQU    09
PC        EQU    02
LNIBL     EQU    0C
```

143

HNIBL	EQU	0D	
STORE	EQU	0E	
CNTR	EQU	0F	
	BSF	STATUS,5	;Select page 1
	CLRF	BDIR	;Set port B outputs
	MOVLW	0xF3	
	MOVWF	ADIR	;Set RA2/3 as digital lines
	MOVLW	02	
	MOVWF	ADCON	;Set RA0/1 as analogue inputs
	BCF	STATUS,5	;Select page 0
MAIN	MOVLW	0xC1	
	MOVWF	ADCON	;Select Ch0/Internal clock
	BSF	ADCON,2	;Start conversion
	NOP		;Wait
	MOVF	ADRES,0	;Place conversion in W
	MOVWF	STORE	;Store conversion
	BCF	STATUS,CARRY	
	SUBLW	63	
	BTFSS	STATUS,CARRY	
	GOTO	OVERLD	;Indicate overload if over 99
	MOVF	STORE,0	
	CALL	TABLE	;Convert to BCD
	MOVWF	LNIBL	
	MOVWF	HNIBL	
	RRF	HNIBL,1	
	RRF	HNIBL,1	
	RRF	HNIBL,1	
	RRF	HNIBL,1	;Shift high nibble into low one
	MOVLW	0F	
	ANDWF	HNIBL,1	;Mask high nibble of HNIBL
	ANDWF	LNIBL,1	;Mask high nibble of LNIBL
	MOVF	HNIBL,0	
	CALL	TABLE2	
	MOVWF	PORTB	;Load high nibble into port B
	BSF	PORTA,2	;Switch on first digit
	MOVLW	0xFF	
	MOVWF	CNTR	
DELAY1	DECFSZ	CNTR,1	
	GOTO	DELAY1	
	BCF	PORTA,2	;Delay and switch off 1st digit

144

```
         MOVF      LNIBL,0
         CALL      TABLE2
         MOVWF     PORTB        ;Load low nibble into port B
         BSF       PORTA,3      ;Switch on second digit
         MOVLW     0xFF
         MOVWF     CNTR
DELAY2   DECFSZ    CNTR,1
         GOTO      DELAY2       ;Delay and switch off 2nd digit
         BCF       PORTA,3      ;Switch off 2nd digit
         GOTO      MAIN         ;Repeat indefinitely
;
OVERLD   MOVLW     40
         MOVWF     PORTB        ;Load — into port B
         BSF       PORTA,2      ;Switch on first digit
         MOVLW     0xFF
         MOVWF     CNTR
DELAY3   DECFSZ    CNTR,1
         GOTO      DELAY3
         BCF       PORTA,2      ;Delay and switch off 1st digit
         BSF       PORTA,3      ;Switch on second digit
         MOVLW     0xFF
         MOVWF     CNTR
DELAY4   DECFSZ    CNTR,1
         GOTO      DELAY4       ;Delay and switch off 2nd digit
         BCF       PORTA,3      ;Switch off 2nd digit
         GOTO      MAIN         ;Return to main routine
;
TABLE    ADDWF     PC,1
         RETLW     00
         RETLW     01
         RETLW     02
         RETLW     03
         RETLW     04
         RETLW     05
         RETLW     06
         RETLW     07
         RETLW     08
         RETLW     09
         RETLW     10
         RETLW     11
```

RETLW	12
RETLW	13
RETLW	14
RETLW	15
RETLW	16
RETLW	17
RETLW	18
RETLW	19
RETLW	20
RETLW	21
RETLW	22
RETLW	23
RETLW	24
RETLW	25
RETLW	26
RETLW	27
RETLW	28
RETLW	29
RETLW	30
RETLW	31
RETLW	32
RETLW	33
RETLW	34
RETLW	35
RETLW	36
RETLW	37
RETLW	38
RETLW	39
RETLW	40
RETLW	41
RETLW	42
RETLW	43
RETLW	44
RETLW	45
RETLW	46
RETLW	47
RETLW	48
RETLW	49
RETLW	50
RETLW	51

RETLW	52
RETLW	53
RETLW	54
RETLW	55
RETLW	56
RETLW	57
RETLW	58
RETLW	59
RETLW	60
RETLW	61
RETLW	62
RETLW	63
RETLW	64
RETLW	65
RETLW	66
RETLW	67
RETLW	68
RETLW	69
RETLW	70
RETLW	71
RETLW	72
RETLW	73
RETLW	74
RETLW	75
RETLW	76
RETLW	77
RETLW	78
RETLW	79
RETLW	80
RETLW	81
RETLW	82
RETLW	83
RETLW	84
RETLW	85
RETLW	86
RETLW	87
RETLW	88
RETLW	89
RETLW	90
RETLW	91

```
            RETLW      92
            RETLW      93
            RETLW      94
            RETLW      95
            RETLW      96
            RETLW      97
            RETLW      98
            RETLW      99
;
TABLE2      ADDWF      PC,1
            RETLW      3F
            RETLW      06
            RETLW      5B
            RETLW      4F
            RETLW      66
            RETLW      6D
            RETLW      7D
            RETLW      07
            RETLW      7F
            RETLW      6F
            END
```

Components For Two-Digit Voltmeter (0 – 9.9V version)
(Figures 3.6, 3.7 and 3.8)

Resistors (all 0.25 watt 5% carbon film)
R1   1M
R2   150k
R3   6k8
R4 to R10   390R (7 off)
R11, R12   3k3 (2 off)

Potentiometer
VR1   220k min hor preset

Capacitors
C1   330p polystyrene or ceramic plate
C2, C3   100n ceramic (2 off)

Semiconductors

IC1	16C71-04
IC2	µA78L05 (+5V 100mA regulator)
TR1,2	BC549 (2 off)
Display 1,2	7 segment common cathode LED display (2 off)

Miscellaneous

Case, circuit board, 18-pin DIL holder, wire, solder, etc.

MIDI Pedal

Most modern electronic musical instruments are equipped with MIDI ports. Probably the main use of these ports is in conjunction with a computer and sequencing software, or possibly with a dedicated sequencer. However, MIDI ports have their uses for 'live' playing and there is a seemingly endless array of MIDI add-ons on offer. The unit featured here is a MIDI pedal which has three foot-operated switches. Operating one of the switches results in the unit transmitting a program change message to the MIDI instrument. The 'program' name is perhaps a bit misleading, and in this context a program is normally a set of sound generator settings, although it can also be something like a set of control settings for a MIDI controlled audio mixer. The three foot-operated switches send MIDI change messages that select programs one, two, and three. In normal use these program numbers would be set up to provide the three sounds needed for the performance (e.g. grand piano, honky-tonk piano, and church organ), and by operating the appropriate pedal it would then be possible to switch to any of these sounds at will. Of course, most instruments permit easy selection of the required program number via the front panel controls, but there is clearly a huge advantage in the 'look no hands' approach provided by a program change pedal.

Circuit Operation

This is a further example of a PIC project where the circuit is very simple indeed, and the software handles the complexities. The full circuit diagram for the MIDI program change pedal

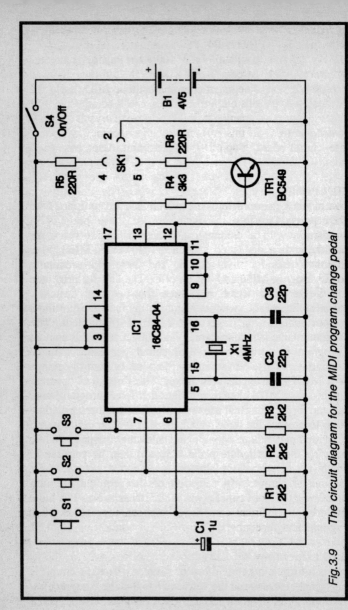

Fig.3.9   The circuit diagram for the MIDI program change pedal

150

appears in Figure 3.9. Unlike the projects described previously, this one does not use a C-R clock oscillator, but instead uses a 4MHz crystal oscillator. The software has to generate a complex pulse stream having accurate timing. It would probably be possible to produce adequate accuracy using a C-R clock provided its output frequency could be adjusted to the correct figure. In practice it is easier to use a crystal controlled clock oscillator, as this ensures adequate accuracy without the need for any setting up of the finished unit. Also, these days a standard frequency crystal such as a 4MHz type costs very little, and opting for a crystal clock circuit does not greatly increase the overall cost of the unit. The only discrete components required for the clock oscillator are C2, C3, and the crystal itself (X1).

Switches S1 to S3 are the three foot-operated switches, and these are used to drive RB0 to RB2 respectively. These inputs are normally taken low by pull-down resistors R1 to R3, but operating one of the switches takes its input high. On the output side, the MIDI output socket (SK1) is driven from RA0 via TR1, which operates as a simple common emitter switch. MIDI is a form of serial interface, which is similar to the standard RS232C type used in computing, etc. However, it operates at the non-standard baud rate of 31250 baud, and it uses a 5mA current loop rather than the positive and negative voltages of a conventional serial link. It is a requirement of the MIDI specification that there is an opto-isolator at every MIDI input, and TR1 drives the LED in the opto-isolator. R5 and R6 provide current limiting in conjunction with a resistor at the MIDI input driven from SK1. Pin 2 at each MIDI output is connected to the earth rail of the equipment, and to the screen of the connecting cable. This prevents the cable from radiating radio frequency interference. The screen is not connected at the MIDI input, as this would provide an electrical connection between the chassis of the sending and receiving devices. Such a connection would be undesirable for a number of reasons, and the opto-isolation is used to avoid any direct electrical connection between the two pieces of equipment.

A 4.5-volt battery supplies power to the circuit, and despite the high clock frequency the current consumption of the circuit is only a few milliamps. The circuit can, of course, be powered from a stabilised 5-volt supply if preferred.

MIDI Basics

The basic action of the software is to monitor the three input lines, and transmit the appropriate two-byte message when one of the lines goes high. The first byte in a MIDI message is the status byte, and this breaks down into two four-bit nibbles. The most significant nibble carries the code that indicates the function of the message, which in this case is 1100 to indicate that it is a program change message. The least significant nibble carries the channel number which is from 0000 (0 decimal) to 1111 (15 decimal). The idea of channelling is to permit messages to be sent to just one instrument in the system, or even to one voice of one instrument. In this application the channel used will not normally be of any importance, and the instrument controlled by the pedal could in fact be set to 'Omni' mode so that it will respond to messages on any channel. The software sends the message on the base channel (0000), but note that the convention is for MIDI channels to be numbered from 1 to 16, and not 0 to 15. Therefore, the message is sent on channel 1 and not channel 0. The software has been written in a way that makes it easy to use another channel if necessary.

With most MIDI messages the status byte is followed by one or more data bytes. In the case of a program change message there is just a single data byte, and this carries the number of the new program. Although an eight-bit byte provides a range of 0 to 255 (decimal), MIDI data bytes always have the most significant bit set to zero. This makes it easy for receiving devices to distinguish status bytes from data bytes, because status bytes always have the most significant bit set to one. A drawback of this method is that limits the range of data values to 0 to 127 (decimal). In this case the data byte has a value of zero, one, or two. The manufacturer of the keyboard instrument might use program numbers from 0 to 127, but some use numbers from 1 to 128, or even something like A-1 to H-8. The manual for the instrument should clearly indicate the relationship between data byte values and the manufacturer's version of program numbers.

Getting the software to generate suitable pulse signals for the MIDI messages is not particularly difficult, and it is basically just a matter of using simple timing loops together with bit set and bit clear instructions. There are a few minor complications that have to be accommodated, and the waveform diagrams of Figure 3.10 should help to explain these. The upper and lower waveforms are those for program change messages to change to program 0 and program 1 respectively. Under standby conditions the output transistor is switched off, but at the start of every byte it is switched on for a period of 32 microseconds. This is called the start bit, and its purpose is to indicate to the receiving device that the data bits are about to follow. The eight data bits are then sent, with each one lasting 32 microseconds. The data bits are sent in sequence, starting with D0 and working through to D7. Note that with a serial signal a high voltage or the current being switched on indicates a 0, and a low voltage or the current being switched off indicates a 1. This is the opposite of what one would probably expect, and is certainly contrary to normal logic conventions. After the final data bit the output transistor is switched off for a period of at least 32 microseconds. This is called the stop bit, and it is really just setting a lower limit on the gap between one byte and the next, which ensures that the receiving device has time to digest one byte before the next one is commenced.

Software

The software has not been written for maximum code efficiency, but has instead been produced in a form that makes it easy to see what is happening. This makes it easy to change the channel or program numbers if desired. The first part of the program sets RA0 as an output and port B as eight inputs. Only three inputs of port B are actually utilized, and the other inputs are tied to earth (they must not be left 'floating'). The main loop simply tests bits 0 to 2 of port B, in turn, to determine whether any of the pushbutton switches have been operated. The program branches to the appropriate subprogram if a button press is detected.

Including the start and stop bits, there are some twenty bits in each two-byte program change message. Each bit is generated by a BSF or BCF instruction followed by a simple

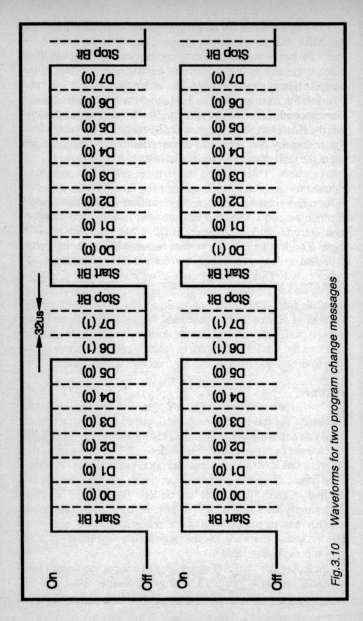

Fig.3.10   Waveforms for two program change messages

timing loop. A BCF instruction is used for a bit that is off (logic 1), and a BSF instruction is used for a bit that is on (logic 0). Each timing loop repeats ten times, and each loop takes three clock cycles. Note that we are not talking here in terms of the basic 4MHz clock cycles, but the clock signal after it has been divided by four internally. This gives a bit length of one microsecond per clock cycle or 30 microseconds in other words. However, there are two further instructions which load the timing counter with the correct value, and this gives the required bit length of 32 microseconds.

Construction
Although this project should not be difficult to construct, there are one or two points that merit amplification. The standard connector for MIDI equipment is the 5 way (180-degree) DIN type. Connection details for this socket are shown in Figure 3.11, which shows the socket viewed from the rear (i.e. looking

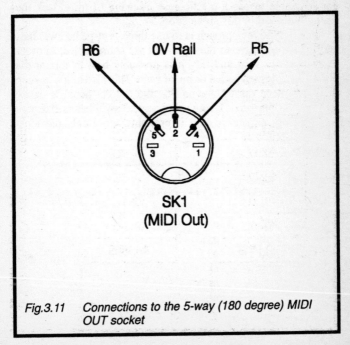

Fig.3.11   Connections to the 5-way (180 degree) MIDI OUT socket

onto the tags to which you will make the soldered connections). Incidentally, most DIN sockets are marked with the pin numbers, but you will almost certainly need a magnifier in order to read them! The MIDI OUT socket of the pedal unit connects to the MIDI IN socket of the keyboard instrument using a standard MIDI cable.

Pushbutton switches S1 to S3 can be large types mounted on the top panel of the case so that they can be operated by foot. The case will then need to be quite large so that the switches can be well spaced out. Otherwise operating one switch may well result in one of the other switches being operated as well. Obviously a fairly tough case would have to be used, and a diecast aluminium type is ideal. However, a suitably large box of this type might be impossible to obtain, or prove to be prohibitively expensive if a suitable type can be located. A folded aluminium box is just about tough enough, and even the larger cases of this type are not very expensive. It is probably not advisable to use a plastic case as many of these lack the strength needed in this application.

An alternative approach is to use three foot-pedal switches, and to connect these to the main unit via short cables. In order to keep things neat and tidy it is probably best to mount the pedals on a large wooden or metal base. This also helps to keep things in place during use so that the correct pedal is easily located and operated. Using proper pedal switches is likely to be relatively expensive, but it probably represents the most practical approach.

```
;*************************************************
;Mk1 MIDI Pedal Program
;*************************************************
;
STATUS      EQU         03
Z           EQU         02
PORTA       EQU         05
PORTB       EQU         06
ADIR        EQU         05
CNTR        EQU         0C
            BSF         STATUS,5      ;Select page 1
            MOVLW       0xFE
```

```
            MOVWF     ADIR       ;Set RA0 as output
            BCF       STATUS,5   ;Select page 0
            CLRF      PORTA      ;Set RA0 low initially
START       BTFSC     PORTB,0    ;Test S1
            GOTO      PRG1
            BTFSC     PORTB,1    ;Test S2
            GOTO      PRG2
            BTFSC     PORTB,2    ;Test S3
            GOTO      PRG3
            GOTO      START      ;Loop until a button is pressed
;
PRG1        BSF       PORTA,0    ;Byte 1 start bit high
            MOVLW     0A
            MOVWF     CNTR
PLS1        DECFSZ    CNTR,1
            GOTO      PLS1
            BSF       PORTA,0    ;Byte 1 D0 high
            MOVLW     0A
            MOVWF     CNTR
PLS2        DECFSZ    CNTR,1
            GOTO      PLS2
            BSF       PORTA,0    ;Byte 1 D1 high
            MOVLW     0A
            MOVWF     CNTR
PLS3        DECFSZ    CNTR,1
            GOTO      PLS3
            BSF       PORTA,0    ;Byte 1 D2 high
            MOVLW     0A
            MOVWF     CNTR
PLS4        DECFSZ    CNTR,1
            GOTO      PLS4
            BSF       PORTA,0    ;Byte 1 D3 high
            MOVLW     0A
            MOVWF     CNTR
PLS5        DECFSZ    CNTR,1
            GOTO      PLS5
            BSF       PORTA,0    ;Byte 1 D4 high
            MOVLW     0A
            MOVWF     CNTR
PLS6        DECFSZ    CNTR,1
```

```
         GOTO    PLS6
         BSF     PORTA,0    ;Byte 1 D5 high
         MOVLW   0A
         MOVWF   CNTR
PLS7     DECFSZ  CNTR,1
         GOTO    PLS7
         BCF     PORTA,0    ;Byte 1 D6 low
         MOVLW   0A
         MOVWF   CNTR
PLS8     DECFSZ  CNTR,1
         GOTO    PLS8
         BCF     PORTA,0    ;Byte 1 D7 low
         MOVLW   0A
         MOVWF   CNTR
PLS9     DECFSZ  CNTR,1
         GOTO    PLS9
         BCF     PORTA,0    ;Byte 1 stop bit low
         MOVLW   0A
         MOVWF   CNTR
PLS10    DECFSZ  CNTR,1
         GOTO    PLS10
         BSF     PORTA,0    ;Byte 2 start bit high
         MOVLW   0A
         MOVWF   CNTR
PLS11    DECFSZ  CNTR,1
         GOTO    PLS11
         BSF     PORTA,0    ;Byte 2 D0 high
         MOVLW   0A
         MOVWF   CNTR
PLS12    DECFSZ  CNTR,1
         GOTO    PLS12
         BSF     PORTA,0    ;Byte 2 D1 high
         MOVLW   0A
         MOVWF   CNTR
PLS13    DECFSZ  CNTR,1
         GOTO    PLS13
         BSF     PORTA,0    ;Byte 2 D2 high
         MOVLW   0A
         MOVWF   CNTR
PLS14    DECFSZ  CNTR,1
```

```
          GOTO      PLS14
          BSF       PORTA,0     ;Byte 1 D3 high
          MOVLW     0A
          MOVWF     CNTR
PLS15     DECFSZ    CNTR,1
          GOTO      PLS15
          BSF       PORTA,0     ;Byte 2 D4 high
          MOVLW     0A
          MOVWF     CNTR
PLS16     DECFSZ    CNTR,1
          GOTO      PLS16
          BSF       PORTA,0     ;Byte 2 D5 high
          MOVLW     0A
          MOVWF     CNTR
PLS17     DECFSZ    CNTR,1
          GOTO      PLS17
          BSF       PORTA,0     ;Byte 2 D6 high
          MOVLW     0A
          MOVWF     CNTR
PLS18     DECFSZ    CNTR,1
          GOTO      PLS18
          BSF       PORTA,0     ;Byte 2 D7 high
          MOVLW     0A
          MOVWF     CNTR
PLS19     DECFSZ    CNTR,1
          GOTO      PLS19
          BCF       PORTA,0     ;Byte 2 stop bit low
          MOVLW     0A
          MOVWF     CNTR
PLS20     DECFSZ    CNTR,1
          GOTO      PLS20
;
REL       MOVF      PORTB,0     ;Wait for button to be released
          BTFSS     STATUS,Z
          GOTO      REL
          GOTO      START       ;Return to main program loop
;
PRG2      BSF       PORTA,0     ;Byte 1 start bit high
          MOVLW     0A
          MOVWF     CNTR
```

159

```
PLS21    DECFSZ    CNTR,1
         GOTO      PLS21
         BSF       PORTA,0    ;Byte 1 D0 high
         MOVLW     0A
         MOVWF     CNTR
PLS22    DECFSZ    CNTR,1
         GOTO      PLS22
         BSF       PORTA,0    ;Byte 1 D1 high
         MOVLW     0A
         MOVWF     CNTR
PLS23    DECFSZ    CNTR,1
         GOTO      PLS23
         BSF       PORTA,0    ;Byte 1 D2 high
         MOVLW     0A
         MOVWF     CNTR
PLS24    DECFSZ    CNTR,1
         GOTO      PLS24
         BSF       PORTA,0    ;Byte 1 D3 high
         MOVLW     0A
         MOVWF     CNTR
PLS25    DECFSZ    CNTR,1
         GOTO      PLS25
         BSF       PORTA,0    ;Byte 1 D4 high
         MOVLW     0A
         MOVWF     CNTR
PLS26    DECFSZ    CNTR,1
         GOTO      PLS26
         BSF       PORTA,0    ;Byte 1 D5 high
         MOVLW     0A
         MOVWF     CNTR
PLS27    DECFSZ    CNTR,1
         GOTO      PLS27
         BCF       PORTA,0    ;Byte 1 D6 low
         MOVLW     0A
         MOVWF     CNTR
PLS28    DECFSZ    CNTR,1
         GOTO      PLS28
         BCF       PORTA,0    ;Byte 1 D7 low
         MOVLW     0A
         MOVWF     CNTR
```

```
PLS29      DECFSZ    CNTR,1
           GOTO      PLS29
           BCF       PORTA,0    ;Byte 1 stop bit low
           MOVLW     0A
           MOVWF     CNTR
PLS30      DECFSZ    CNTR,1
           GOTO      PLS30
           BSF       PORTA,0    ;Byte 2 start bit high
           MOVLW     0A
           MOVWF     CNTR
PLS31      DECFSZ    CNTR,1
           GOTO      PLS31
           BCF       PORTA,0    ;Byte 2 D0 low
           MOVLW     0A
           MOVWF     CNTR
PLS32      DECFSZ    CNTR,1
           GOTO      PLS32
           BSF       PORTA,0    ;Byte 2 D1 high
           MOVLW     0A
           MOVWF     CNTR
PLS33      DECFSZ    CNTR,1
           GOTO      PLS33
           BSF       PORTA,0    ;Byte 2 D2 high
           MOVLW     0A
           MOVWF     CNTR
PLS34      DECFSZ    CNTR,1
           GOTO      PLS34
           BSF       PORTA,0    ;Byte 1 D3 high
           MOVLW     0A
           MOVWF     CNTR
PLS35      DECFSZ    CNTR,1
           GOTO      PLS35
           BSF       PORTA,0    ;Byte 2 D4 high
           MOVLW     0A
           MOVWF     CNTR
PLS36      DECFSZ    CNTR,1
           GOTO      PLS36
           BSF       PORTA,0    ;Byte 2 D5 high
           MOVLW     0A
           MOVWF     CNTR
```

PLS37	DECFSZ	CNTR,1	
	GOTO	PLS17	
	BSF	PORTA,0	;Byte 2 D6 high
	MOVLW	0A	
	MOVWF	CNTR	
PLS38	DECFSZ	CNTR,1	
	GOTO	PLS38	
	BSF	PORTA,0	;Byte 2 D7 high
	MOVLW	0A	
	MOVWF	CNTR	
PLS39	DECFSZ	CNTR,1	
	GOTO	PLS39	
	BCF	PORTA,0	;Byte 2 stop bit low
	MOVLW	0A	
	MOVWF	CNTR	
PLS40	DECFSZ	CNTR,1	
	GOTO	PLS40	
;			
REL2	MOVF	PORTB,0	;Wait for button to be released
	BTFSS	STATUS,Z	
	GOTO	REL2	
	GOTO	START	;Return to main program loop
;			
PRG3	BSF	PORTA,0	;Byte 1 start bit high
	MOVLW	0A	
	MOVWF	CNTR	
PLS41	DECFSZ	CNTR,1	
	GOTO	PLS41	
	BSF	PORTA,0	;Byte 1 D0 high
	MOVLW	0A	
	MOVWF	CNTR	
PLS42	DECFSZ	CNTR,1	
	GOTO	PLS42	
	BSF	PORTA,0	;Byte 1 D1 high
	MOVLW	0A	
	MOVWF	CNTR	
PLS43	DECFSZ	CNTR,1	
	GOTO	PLS43	
	BSF	PORTA,0	;Byte 1 D2 high
	MOVLW	0A	

162

	MOVWF	CNTR	
PLS44	DECFSZ	CNTR,1	
	GOTO	PLS44	
	BSF	PORTA,0	;Byte 1 D3 high
	MOVLW	0A	
	MOVWF	CNTR	
PLS45	DECFSZ	CNTR,1	
	GOTO	PLS45	
	BSF	PORTA,0	;Byte 1 D4 high
	MOVLW	0A	
	MOVWF	CNTR	
PLS46	DECFSZ	CNTR,1	
	GOTO	PLS46	
	BSF	PORTA,0	;Byte 1 D5 high
	MOVLW	0A	
	MOVWF	CNTR	
PLS47	DECFSZ	CNTR,1	
	GOTO	PLS47	
	BCF	PORTA,0	;Byte 1 D6 low
	MOVLW	0A	
	MOVWF	CNTR	
PLS48	DECFSZ	CNTR,1	
	GOTO	PLS48	
	BCF	PORTA,0	;Byte 1 D7 low
	MOVLW	0A	
	MOVWF	CNTR	
PLS49	DECFSZ	CNTR,1	
	GOTO	PLS49	
	BCF	PORTA,0	;Byte 1 stop bit low
	MOVLW	0A	
	MOVWF	CNTR	
PLS50	DECFSZ	CNTR,1	
	GOTO	PLS50	
	BSF	PORTA,0	;Byte 2 start bit high
	MOVLW	0A	
	MOVWF	CNTR	
PLS51	DECFSZ	CNTR,1	
	GOTO	PLS51	
	BSF	PORTA,0	;Byte 2 D0 high
	MOVLW	0A	

	MOVWF	CNTR	
PLS52	DECFSZ	CNTR,1	
	GOTO	PLS52	
	BCF	PORTA,0	;Byte 2 D1 low
	MOVLW	0A	
	MOVWF	CNTR	
PLS53	DECFSZ	CNTR,1	
	GOTO	PLS53	
	BSF	PORTA,0	;Byte 2 D2 high
	MOVLW	0A	
	MOVWF	CNTR	
PLS54	DECFSZ	CNTR,1	
	GOTO	PLS54	
	BSF	PORTA,0	;Byte 1 D3 high
	MOVLW	0A	
	MOVWF	CNTR	
PLS55	DECFSZ	CNTR,1	
	GOTO	PLS55	
	BSF	PORTA,0	;Byte 2 D4 high
	MOVLW	0A	
	MOVWF	CNTR	
PLS56	DECFSZ	CNTR,1	
	GOTO	PLS56	
	BSF	PORTA,0	;Byte 2 D5 high
	MOVLW	0A	
	MOVWF	CNTR	
PLS57	DECFSZ	CNTR,1	
	GOTO	PLS57	
	BSF	PORTA,0	;Byte 2 D6 high
	MOVLW	0A	
	MOVWF	CNTR	
PLS58	DECFSZ	CNTR,1	
	GOTO	PLS58	
	BSF	PORTA,0	;Byte 2 D7 high
	MOVLW	0A	
	MOVWF	CNTR	
PLS59	DECFSZ	CNTR,1	
	GOTO	PLS59	
	BCF	PORTA,0	;Byte 2 stop bit low
	MOVLW	0A	

```
          MOVWF     CNTR
PLS60     DECFSZ    CNTR,1
          GOTO      PLS60
;
REL3      MOVF      PORTB,0    ;Wait for button to be released
          BTFSS     STATUS,Z
          GOTO      REL3
          GOTO      START      ;Return to main program loop
          END
```

Components for MIDI Pedal (Figure 3.9)

Resistors (all 0.25 watt 5% carbon film)
R1, R2, R3   2k2 (3 off)
R4   3k3
R5, R6   220R (2 off)

Capacitors
C1   1µ 50V elect
C2, C3   22p ceramic plate (2 off)

Semiconductors
IC1   PIC 16C84-04
TR1   BC549

Miscellaneous
X1   4MHz wire-ended crystal
B1   4V5 (3 × AA size cells in holder)
S1, S2, S3   Push-to-make switches (3 off - see text)
S4   s.p.s.t. min toggle switch
SK1   5-way 180-degree DIN socket
Case, circuit board, 18-pin DIL holder, battery connector (PP3
type), wire, solder, etc.

MIDI Pedal – 2
Using a PIC processor based circuit it is possible to produce a
MIDI pedal that will send practically any desired MIDI
message. This MIDI pedal uses exactly the same circuit as the

one described previously, but uses a different program to give it a very different function. Most modern MIDI instruments can be set to conform to the General MIDI standard, and in this mode there is a standard sound assigned to each program number. Furthermore, channel 10 is set aside for percussion sounds, with each note assigned to a different percussion sound. The point of this system is that it enables a large number of different percussion sounds to be used, but these sounds only occupy one MIDI channel. Only sounds that do not have a specific pitch are catered for by channel 10, but this encompasses many popular percussion instruments such as cymbal crashes and hand claps. The other MIDI channels are used to handle percussion sounds that must be played at a specific pitch.

Each footswitch on this MIDI pedal activates a different 'note' on channel 10, which in practice means that operating each pedal produces a different percussion sound from the synthesiser. The notes used in the example program are 39, 49, and 54, which respectively correspond to hand clap, crash cymbal, and tambourine sounds. However, the program is easily modified to accommodate any three of the available sounds.

Two MIDI messages are needed to produce a note, and the first of these is the note on message. This has 1001 as the most significant nibble in the status byte, and the channel number in the least significant nibble. The status byte is followed by two data bytes, which carry the note and velocity values. With a keyboard instrument the velocity value indicates how hard a key was played. It is of no practical significance with a simple MIDI pedal, and the convention is to use a dummy velocity value of 64 (i.e. about half the maximum value of 127). Notes must not be left playing indefinitely, and all note on messages must be followed in due course by corresponding note off messages. A note off message follows along the same lines as a note on type, but the most significant nibble in the status byte is 1000 rather than 1001. When the pedal is activated it must therefore produce a three byte note on message, wait briefly, and then produce a three byte note off message.

Software

The method of monitoring the switches and producing each bit of the serial signal is much the same as in the original MIDI pedal program. Overall operation of the program is rather different though. Each byte of the two MIDI messages is defined in a separate subroutine. When the main loop detects that one of the switches has been activated it branches to a subprogram that calls up the appropriate subroutines to produce the required bytes for the MIDI message. In addition to the subroutines that produce the serial bytes there is a further subroutine that produces the delay between each pair of note on and note off messages. Also, there is a subroutine that monitors the switch and prevents the program from re-entering the main loop until the switch has been released. A further delay is provided after this to give contact de-bouncing.

The subroutines that control the notes activated by S1 to S3 are NT1, NT2, and NT3 respectively. These can be modified to activate any of the available notes/percussion sounds. This is a list of the available sounds and the note values that produce them. Many of the 128 note values have not been assigned percussion sounds incidentally.

Program No.	Percussion Sound
35	Acoustic Bass Drum
36	Bass Drum 1
37	Side Stick
38	Acoustic Snare
39	Hand Clap
40	Electric Snare
41	Low Floor Tom
42	Closed Hi-Hat
43	High Floor Tom
44	Pedal Hi-Hat
45	Low Tom
46	Open Hi-Hat
47	Low Mid Tom
48	High Mid Tom
49	Crash Cymbal 1
50	High Tom
51	Ride Cymbal 1

52	Chinese Cymbal
53	Ride Bell
54	Tambourine
55	Splash Cymbal
56	Cowbell
57	Crash Cymbal 2
58	Vibraslap
59	Ride Cymbal 2
60	High Bongo
61	Low Bongo
62	Mute Hi Conga
63	Open Hi Conga
64	Low Conga
65	High Timbale
66	Low Timbale
67	High Agogo
68	Low Agogo 2
69	Cabasa
70	Maracas
71	Short Whistle
72	Long Whistle
73	Short Guiro
74	Long Guiro
75	Claves
76	High Woodblock
77	Low Woodblock
78	Mute Cuica
79	Open Cuica
80	Mute Triangle
81	Open Triangle

```
;************************************************
;Mk2 MIDI Pedal Program
;************************************************
;
STATUS      EQU        03
Z           EQU        02
PORTA       EQU        05
PORTB       EQU        06
```

```
ADIR      EQU      05
CNTR      EQU      0C
CNTR2     EQU      0D
          BSF      STATUS,5   ;Select page 1
          MOVLW    0xFE
          MOVWF    ADIR       ;Set RA0 as output
          BCF      STATUS,5   ;Select page 0
          CLRF     PORTA      ;Set RA0 low initially
START     BTFSC    PORTB,0    ;Test S1
          GOTO     DRM1
          BTFSC    PORTB,1    ;Test S2
          GOTO     DRM2
          BTFSC    PORTB,2    ;Test S3
          GOTO     DRM3
          GOTO     START      ;Loop until a button is pressed
;
DRM1      CALL     NTON
          CALL     NT1
          CALL     VELO
          CALL     DEL
          CALL     NTOFF
          CALL     NT1
          CALL     VELO
          CALL     REL
          CALL     DEL
          GOTO     START
;
DRM2      CALL     NTON
          CALL     NT2
          CALL     VELO
          CALL     DEL
          CALL     NTOFF
          CALL     NT1
          CALL     VELO
          CALL     REL
          CALL     DEL
          GOTO     START
;
DRM3      CALL     NTON
          CALL     NT3
```

169

```
         CALL      VELO
         CALL      DEL
         CALL      NTOFF
         CALL      NT1
         CALL      VELO
         CALL      REL
         CALL      DEL
         GOTO      START
;
NTON     BSF       PORTA,0    ;Byte 1 start bit high
         MOVLW     0A
         MOVWF     CNTR
PLS1     DECFSZ    CNTR,1
         GOTO      PLS1
         BCF       PORTA,0    ;Byte 1 D0 low
         MOVLW     0A
         MOVWF     CNTR
PLS2     DECFSZ    CNTR,1
         GOTO      PLS2
         BSF       PORTA,0    ;Byte 1 D1 high
         MOVLW     0A
         MOVWF     CNTR
PLS3     DECFSZ    CNTR,1
         GOTO      PLS3
         BSF       PORTA,0    ;Byte 1 D2 high
         MOVLW     0A
         MOVWF     CNTR
PLS4     DECFSZ    CNTR,1
         GOTO      PLS4
         BCF       PORTA,0    ;Byte 1 D3 low
         MOVLW     0A
         MOVWF     CNTR
PLS5     DECFSZ    CNTR,1
         GOTO      PLS5
         BCF       PORTA,0    ;Byte 1 D4 low
         MOVLW     0A
         MOVWF     CNTR
PLS6     DECFSZ    CNTR,1
         GOTO      PLS6
         BSF       PORTA,0    ;Byte 1 D5 high
```

```
        MOVLW    0A
        MOVWF    CNTR
PLS7    DECFSZ   CNTR,1
        GOTO     PLS7
        BSF      PORTA,0    ;Byte 1 D6 high
        MOVLW    0A
        MOVWF    CNTR
PLS8    DECFSZ   CNTR,1
        GOTO     PLS8
        BCF      PORTA,0    ;Byte 1 D7 low
        MOVLW    0A
        MOVWF    CNTR
PLS9    DECFSZ   CNTR,1
        GOTO     PLS9
        BCF      PORTA,0    ;Byte 1 stop bit low
        MOVLW    0A
        MOVWF    CNTR
PLS10   DECFSZ   CNTR,1
        GOTO     PLS10
        RETURN
;
NT1     BSF      PORTA,0    ;Byte 2 start bit high
        MOVLW    0A
        MOVWF    CNTR
PLS11   DECFSZ   CNTR,1
        GOTO     PLS11
        BCF      PORTA,0    ;Byte 2 D0 low
        MOVLW    0A
        MOVWF    CNTR
PLS12   DECFSZ   CNTR,1
        GOTO     PLS12
        BSF      PORTA,0    ;Byte 2 D1 high
        MOVLW    0A
        MOVWF    CNTR
PLS13   DECFSZ   CNTR,1
        GOTO     PLS13
        BSF      PORTA,0    ;Byte 2 D2 high
        MOVLW    0A
        MOVWF    CNTR
PLS14   DECFSZ   CNTR,1
```

```
              GOTO     PLS14
              BSF      PORTA,0    ;Byte 1 D3 high
              MOVLW    0A
              MOVWF    CNTR
PLS15         DECFSZ   CNTR,1
              GOTO     PLS15
              BCF      PORTA,0    ;Byte 2 D4 low
              MOVLW    0A
              MOVWF    CNTR
PLS16         DECFSZ   CNTR,1
              GOTO     PLS16
              BCF      PORTA,0    ;Byte 2 D5 low
              MOVLW    0A
              MOVWF    CNTR
PLS17         DECFSZ   CNTR,1
              GOTO     PLS17
              BSF      PORTA,0    ;Byte 2 D6 high
              MOVLW    0A
              MOVWF    CNTR
PLS18         DECFSZ   CNTR,1
              GOTO     PLS18
              BSF      PORTA,0    ;Byte 2 D7 high
              MOVLW    0A
              MOVWF    CNTR
PLS19         DECFSZ   CNTR,1
              GOTO     PLS19
              BCF      PORTA,0    ;Byte 2 stop bit low
              MOVLW    0A
              MOVWF    CNTR
PLS20         DECFSZ   CNTR,1
              GOTO     PLS20
              RETURN
;
NT2           BSF      PORTA,0    ;Byte 2 start bit high
              MOVLW    0A
              MOVWF    CNTR
PLS41         DECFSZ   CNTR,1
              GOTO     PLS41
              BCF      PORTA,0    ;Byte 2 D0 low
              MOVLW    0A
```

```
        MOVWF   CNTR
PLS42   DECFSZ  CNTR,1
        GOTO    PLS42
        BCF     PORTA,0     ;Byte 2 D1 low
        MOVLW   0A
        MOVWF   CNTR
PLS43   DECFSZ  CNTR,1
        GOTO    PLS43
        BCF     PORTA,0     ;Byte 2 D2 low
        MOVLW   0A
        MOVWF   CNTR
PLS44   DECFSZ  CNTR,1
        GOTO    PLS44
        BSF     PORTA,0     ;Byte 1 D3 high
        MOVLW   0A
        MOVWF   CNTR
PLS45   DECFSZ  CNTR,1
        GOTO    PLS45
        BSF     PORTA,0     ;Byte 2 D4 high
        MOVLW   0A
        MOVWF   CNTR
PLS46   DECFSZ  CNTR,1
        GOTO    PLS46
        BCF     PORTA,0     ;Byte 2 D5 low
        MOVLW   0A
        MOVWF   CNTR
PLS47   DECFSZ  CNTR,1
        GOTO    PLS47
        BSF     PORTA,0     ;Byte 2 D6 high
        MOVLW   0A
        MOVWF   CNTR
PLS48   DECFSZ  CNTR,1
        GOTO    PLS48
        BSF     PORTA,0     ;Byte 2 D7 high
        MOVLW   0A
        MOVWF   CNTR
PLS49   DECFSZ  CNTR,1
        GOTO    PLS49
        BCF     PORTA,0     ;Byte 2 stop bit low
        MOVLW   0A
```

```
                MOVWF    CNTR
PLS50           DECFSZ   CNTR,1
                GOTO     PLS50
                RETURN
;
NT3             BSF      PORTA,0    ;Byte 2 start bit high
                MOVLW    0A
                MOVWF    CNTR
PLS51           DECFSZ   CNTR,1
                GOTO     PLS51
                BSF      PORTA,0    ;Byte 2 D0 high
                MOVLW    0A
                MOVWF    CNTR
PLS52           DECFSZ   CNTR,1
                GOTO     PLS52
                BCF      PORTA,0    ;Byte 2 D1 low
                MOVLW    0A
                MOVWF    CNTR
PLS53           DECFSZ   CNTR,1
                GOTO     PLS53
                BCF      PORTA,0    ;Byte 2 D2 low
                MOVLW    0A
                MOVWF    CNTR
PLS54           DECFSZ   CNTR,1
                GOTO     PLS54
                BSF      PORTA,0    ;Byte 1 D3 high
                MOVLW    0A
                MOVWF    CNTR
PLS55           DECFSZ   CNTR,1
                GOTO     PLS55
                BCF      PORTA,0    ;Byte 2 D4 low
                MOVLW    0A
                MOVWF    CNTR
PLS56           DECFSZ   CNTR,1
                GOTO     PLS56
                BCF      PORTA,0    ;Byte 2 D5 low
                MOVLW    0A
                MOVWF    CNTR
PLS57           DECFSZ   CNTR,1
                GOTO     PLS57
```

```
            BSF      PORTA,0   ;Byte 2 D6 high
            MOVLW    0A
            MOVWF    CNTR
PLS58       DECFSZ   CNTR,1
            GOTO     PLS58
            BSF      PORTA,0   ;Byte 2 D7 high
            MOVLW    0A
            MOVWF    CNTR
PLS59       DECFSZ   CNTR,1
            GOTO     PLS59
            BCF      PORTA,0   ;Byte 2 stop bit low
            MOVLW    0A
            MOVWF    CNTR
PLS60       DECFSZ   CNTR,1
            GOTO     PLS60
            RETURN
;
REL         MOVF     PORTB,0   ;Wait for button to be released
            BTFSS    STATUS,Z
            GOTO     REL
            RETURN
;
VELO        BSF      PORTA,0   ;Byte 3 start bit high
            MOVLW    0A
            MOVWF    CNTR
PLS21       DECFSZ   CNTR,1
            GOTO     PLS21
            BSF      PORTA,0   ;Byte 3 D0 high
            MOVLW    0A
            MOVWF    CNTR
PLS22       DECFSZ   CNTR,1
            GOTO     PLS22
            BSF      PORTA,0   ;Byte 3 D1 high
            MOVLW    0A
            MOVWF    CNTR
PLS23       DECFSZ   CNTR,1
            GOTO     PLS23
            BSF      PORTA,0   ;Byte 3 D2 high
            MOVLW    0A
            MOVWF    CNTR
```

175

```
PLS24    DECFSZ    CNTR,1
         GOTO      PLS24
         BSF       PORTA,0    ;Byte 3 D3 high
         MOVLW     0A
         MOVWF     CNTR
PLS25    DECFSZ    CNTR,1
         GOTO      PLS25
         BSF       PORTA,0    ;Byte 3 D4 high
         MOVLW     0A
         MOVWF     CNTR
PLS26    DECFSZ    CNTR,1
         GOTO      PLS26
         BSF       PORTA,0    ;Byte 3 D5 high
         MOVLW     0A
         MOVWF     CNTR
PLS27    DECFSZ    CNTR,1
         GOTO      PLS27
         BCF       PORTA,0    ;Byte 3 D6 low
         MOVLW     0A
         MOVWF     CNTR
PLS28    DECFSZ    CNTR,1
         GOTO      PLS28
         BSF       PORTA,0    ;Byte 3 D7 high
         MOVLW     0A
         MOVWF     CNTR
PLS29    DECFSZ    CNTR,1
         GOTO      PLS29
         BCF       PORTA,0    ;Byte 3 stop bit low
         MOVLW     0A
         MOVWF     CNTR
PLS30    DECFSZ    CNTR,1
         GOTO      PLS30
         RETURN
;
NTOFF    BSF       PORTA,0    ;Byte 1 start bit high
         MOVLW     0A
         MOVWF     CNTR
PLS31    DECFSZ    CNTR,1
         GOTO      PLS31
         BCF       PORTA,0    ;Byte 1 D0 low
```

```
         MOVLW    0A
         MOVWF    CNTR
PLS32    DECFSZ   CNTR,1
         GOTO     PLS32
         BSF      PORTA,0    ;Byte 1 D1 high
         MOVLW    0A
         MOVWF    CNTR
PLS33    DECFSZ   CNTR,1
         GOTO     PLS33
         BSF      PORTA,0    ;Byte 1 D2 high
         MOVLW    0A
         MOVWF    CNTR
PLS34    DECFSZ   CNTR,1
         GOTO     PLS34
         BCF      PORTA,0    ;Byte 1 D3 low
         MOVLW    0A
         MOVWF    CNTR
PLS35    DECFSZ   CNTR,1
         GOTO     PLS35
         BSF      PORTA,0    ;Byte 1 D4 high
         MOVLW    0A
         MOVWF    CNTR
PLS36    DECFSZ   CNTR,1
         GOTO     PLS36
         BSF      PORTA,0    ;Byte 1 D5 high
         MOVLW    0A
         MOVWF    CNTR
PLS37    DECFSZ   CNTR,1
         GOTO     PLS17
         BSF      PORTA,0    ;Byte 1 D6 high
         MOVLW    0A
         MOVWF    CNTR
PLS38    DECFSZ   CNTR,1
         GOTO     PLS38
         BCF      PORTA,0    ;Byte 1 D7 low
         MOVLW    0A
         MOVWF    CNTR
PLS39    DECFSZ   CNTR,1
         GOTO     PLS39
         BCF      PORTA,0    ;Byte 1 stop bit low
```

```
          MOVLW      0A
          MOVWF      CNTR
PLS40     DECFSZ     CNTR,1
          GOTO       PLS40
;
DEL       MOVLW      0xFF
          MOVWF      CNTR
          MOVLW      50
          MOVWF      CNTR2
DEL1      DECFSZ     CNTR,1
          GOTO       DEL1
          DECFSZ     CNTR2,1
          GOTO       DEL1
          RETURN
;
          END
```

Components
The same as for the Mk 1 MIDI pedal (see the previous section of this chapter.

MIDI Pedal – 3

This third version of the MIDI pedal uses the slightly modified circuit as shown in Figure 3.12. It differs from the original circuit (Figure 3.9) in that only one foot operated switch is used (S1), and this has some electrical de-bouncing in the form of R1 and C2. The purpose of this pedal is to generate a MIDI control change message. Specifically, it is a sustain pedal. The control change message is another three-byte type, and it has 1011 as the most significant nibble of the status byte. As usual for a channel message, the least significant nibble of the status byte carries the channel number. The software listing provided here uses 0000 (channel 1) for the channel nibble, but this could obviously be changed if necessary. Two data bytes follow the status byte, and these contain the control number and the new value for the control. In this case a control number of 64 (decimal) is used, and this is the standard control number for the sustain function. Of course, not all MIDI instruments support this feature, so check the MIDI implementation charts

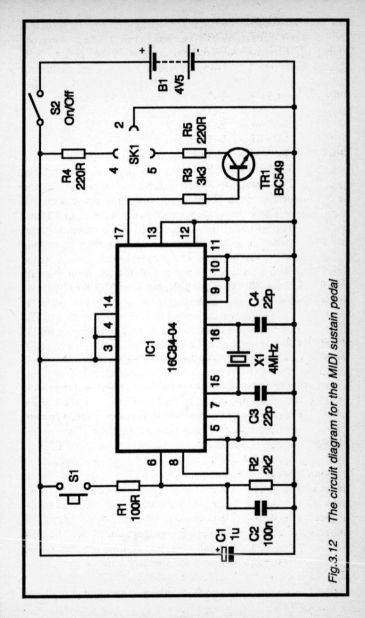

Fig.3.12   The circuit diagram for the MIDI sustain pedal

179

for your instruments before constructing this unit. The sustain function is a simple on/off type, and the data byte is therefore either 127 (decimal) to turn the sustain on, or 0 to switch it off. The software must therefore generate a control message having 127 as the final data byte when S1 is closed, and a further control message having 0 as the final data byte when S1 is released.

Software

The way in which this program generates the three-byte messages is much the same as the one used in the previous program. The main loop detects that S1 has been pressed, and it then branches to a subprogram that calls up a series of subroutines. These subroutines generate the serial output signal on RA0. The program then loops until S1 is released, after which a further three-byte message is put together by calling the appropriate subroutines. The program then returns to the main loop and monitors S1 once again. The program is easily modified to handle other controls, but few (if any) others are implemented by most instruments. A portamento pedal is sometimes implemented as control number 65, and the unit can be converted to control this function merely by changing bit D0 in the control number ('CONNO') subroutine. The BSF instruction here should be changed to a BCF type.

```
;************************************************
;Mk3 MIDI Pedal Program
;************************************************
;
STATUS    EQU        03
Z         EQU        02
PORTA     EQU        05
PORTB     EQU        06
ADIR      EQU        05
CNTR      EQU        0C
          BSF        STATUS,5   ;Select page 1
          MOVLW      0xFE
          MOVWF      ADIR       ;Set RA0 as output
          BCF        STATUS,5   ;Select page 0
          CLRF       PORTA      ;Set RA0 low initially
```

```
START     BTFSC    PORTB,0    ;Test S1
          GOTO     PEDON
          GOTO     START      ;Loop until a button is pressed
;
PEDON     CALL     CONCH      ;Control change status byte
          CALL     CONNO      ;Control number byte (64)
          CALL     ONDATA     ;Control on data byte
LOOP      BTFSC    PORTB,0    ;Test S1
          GOTO     LOOP       ;Loop until S1 is released
          CALL     CONCH      ;Control change status byte
          CALL     CONNO      ;Control number byte (64)
          CALL     OFFDATA    ;Control off data byte
          GOTO     START      ;Loop indefinitely
;
CONCH     BSF      PORTA,0    ;Byte 1 start bit high
          MOVLW    0A
          MOVWF    CNTR
PLS1      DECFSZ   CNTR,1
          GOTO     PLS1
          BSF      PORTA,0    ;Byte 1 D0 high
          MOVLW    0A
          MOVWF    CNTR
PLS2      DECFSZ   CNTR,1
          GOTO     PLS2
          BSF      PORTA,0    ;Byte 1 D1 high
          MOVLW    0A
          MOVWF    CNTR
PLS3      DECFSZ   CNTR,1
          GOTO     PLS3
          BSF      PORTA,0    ;Byte 1 D2 high
          MOVLW    0A
          MOVWF    CNTR
PLS4      DECFSZ   CNTR,1
          GOTO     PLS4
          BSF      PORTA,0    ;Byte 1 D3 high
          MOVLW    0A
          MOVWF    CNTR
PLS5      DECFSZ   CNTR,1
          GOTO     PLS5
          BCF      PORTA,0    ;Byte 1 D4 low
```

181

```
        MOVLW    0A
        MOVWF    CNTR
PLS6    DECFSZ   CNTR,1
        GOTO     PLS6
        BCF      PORTA,0    ;Byte 1 D5 low
        MOVLW    0A
        MOVWF    CNTR
PLS7    DECFSZ   CNTR,1
        GOTO     PLS7
        BSF      PORTA,0    ;Byte 1 D6 high
        MOVLW    0A
        MOVWF    CNTR
PLS8    DECFSZ   CNTR,1
        GOTO     PLS8
        BCF      PORTA,0    ;Byte 1 D7 low
        MOVLW    0A
        MOVWF    CNTR
PLS9    DECFSZ   CNTR,1
        GOTO     PLS9
        BCF      PORTA,0    ;Byte 1 stop bit low
        MOVLW    0A
        MOVWF    CNTR
PLS10   DECFSZ   CNTR,1
        GOTO     PLS10
        RETURN
;
CONNO   BSF      PORTA,0    ;Byte 2 start bit high
        MOVLW    0A
        MOVWF    CNTR
PLS11   DECFSZ   CNTR,1
        GOTO     PLS11
        BSF      PORTA,0    ;Byte 2 D0 high
        MOVLW    0A
        MOVWF    CNTR
PLS12   DECFSZ   CNTR,1
        GOTO     PLS12
        BSF      PORTA,0    ;Byte 2 D1high
        MOVLW    0A
        MOVWF    CNTR
PLS13   DECFSZ   CNTR,1
```

```
          GOTO      PLS13
          BSF       PORTA,0    ;Byte 2 D2 high
          MOVLW     0A
          MOVWF     CNTR
PLS14     DECFSZ    CNTR,1
          GOTO      PLS14
          BSF       PORTA,0    ;Byte 1 D3 high
          MOVLW     0A
          MOVWF     CNTR
PLS15     DECFSZ    CNTR,1
          GOTO      PLS15
          BSF       PORTA,0    ;Byte 2 D4 high
          MOVLW     0A
          MOVWF     CNTR
PLS16     DECFSZ    CNTR,1
          GOTO      PLS16
          BSF       PORTA,0    ;Byte 2 D5 high
          MOVLW     0A
          MOVWF     CNTR
PLS17     DECFSZ    CNTR,1
          GOTO      PLS17
          BCF       PORTA,0    ;Byte 2 D6 low
          MOVLW     0A
          MOVWF     CNTR
PLS18     DECFSZ    CNTR,1
          GOTO      PLS18
          BSF       PORTA,0    ;Byte 2 D7 high
          MOVLW     0A
          MOVWF     CNTR
PLS19     DECFSZ    CNTR,1
          GOTO      PLS19
          BCF       PORTA,0    ;Byte 2 stop bit low
          MOVLW     0A
          MOVWF     CNTR
PLS20     DECFSZ    CNTR,1
          GOTO      PLS20
          RETURN
;
ONDATA    BSF       PORTA,0    ;Byte 3 start bit high
          MOVLW     0A
```

	MOVWF	CNTR	
PLS21	DECFSZ	CNTR,1	
	GOTO	PLS21	
	BCF	PORTA,0	;Byte 3 D0 low
	MOVLW	0A	
	MOVWF	CNTR	
PLS22	DECFSZ	CNTR,1	
	GOTO	PLS22	
	BCF	PORTA,0	;Byte 3 D1 low
	MOVLW	0A	
	MOVWF	CNTR	
PLS23	DECFSZ	CNTR,1	
	GOTO	PLS23	
	BCF	PORTA,0	;Byte 3 D2 low
	MOVLW	0A	
	MOVWF	CNTR	
PLS24	DECFSZ	CNTR,1	
	GOTO	PLS24	
	BCF	PORTA,0	;Byte 3 D3 low
	MOVLW	0A	
	MOVWF	CNTR	
PLS25	DECFSZ	CNTR,1	
	GOTO	PLS25	
	BCF	PORTA,0	;Byte 3 D4 low
	MOVLW	0A	
	MOVWF	CNTR	
PLS26	DECFSZ	CNTR,1	
	GOTO	PLS26	
	BCF	PORTA,0	;Byte 3 D5 low
	MOVLW	0A	
	MOVWF	CNTR	
PLS27	DECFSZ	CNTR,1	
	GOTO	PLS27	
	BCF	PORTA,0	;Byte 3 D6 low
	MOVLW	0A	
	MOVWF	CNTR	
PLS28	DECFSZ	CNTR,1	
	GOTO	PLS28	
	BSF	PORTA,0	;Byte 3 D7 high
	MOVLW	0A	

184

```
          MOVWF    CNTR
PLS29     DECFSZ   CNTR,1
          GOTO     PLS29
          BCF      PORTA,0    ;Byte 3 stop bit low
          MOVLW    0A
          MOVWF    CNTR
PLS30     DECFSZ   CNTR,1
          GOTO     PLS30
          RETURN
;
OFFDATA   BSF      PORTA,0    ;Byte 1 start bit high
          MOVLW    0A
          MOVWF    CNTR
PLS31     DECFSZ   CNTR,1
          GOTO     PLS31
          BSF      PORTA,0    ;Byte 1 D0 high
          MOVLW    0A
          MOVWF    CNTR
PLS32     DECFSZ   CNTR,1
          GOTO     PLS32
          BSF      PORTA,0    ;Byte 1 D1 high
          MOVLW    0A
          MOVWF    CNTR
PLS33     DECFSZ   CNTR,1
          GOTO     PLS33
          BSF      PORTA,0    ;Byte 1 D2 high
          MOVLW    0A
          MOVWF    CNTR
PLS34     DECFSZ   CNTR,1
          GOTO     PLS34
          BSF      PORTA,0    ;Byte 1 D3 high
          MOVLW    0A
          MOVWF    CNTR
PLS35     DECFSZ   CNTR,1
          GOTO     PLS35
          BSF      PORTA,0    ;Byte 1 D4 high
          MOVLW    0A
          MOVWF    CNTR
PLS36     DECFSZ   CNTR,1
          GOTO     PLS36
```

```
        BSF        PORTA,0    ;Byte 1 D5 high
        MOVLW      0A
        MOVWF      CNTR
PLS37   DECFSZ     CNTR,1
        GOTO       PLS37
        BSF        PORTA,0    ;Byte 1 D6 high
        MOVLW      0A
        MOVWF      CNTR
PLS38   DECFSZ     CNTR,1
        GOTO       PLS38
        BSF        PORTA,0    ;Byte 1 D7 high
        MOVLW      0A
        MOVWF      CNTR
PLS39   DECFSZ     CNTR,1
        GOTO       PLS39
        BCF        PORTA,0    ;Byte 1 stop bit low
        MOVLW      0A
        MOVWF      CNTR
PLS40   DECFSZ     CNTR,1
        GOTO       PLS40
;
        END
```

Components for Mk3 MIDI Pedal (Figure 3.12)

Resistors (all 0.25 watt 5% carbon film)
R1	100R
R2	2k2
R3	3k3
R4, R5	220R (2 off)

Capacitors
C1	1µ 50V elect
C2	100n polyester
C3, C4	22p ceramic plate (2 off)

Semiconductors
IC1	16C84-04
TR1	BC549

Miscellaneous

S1	Push-to-make switch
S2	s.p.s.t. min toggle switch
B1	4V5 (3 × AA size cells in holder)
X1	4MHz wire-ended crystal
SK1	5 way 180 degree DIN socket

Case, circuit board, 18-pin DIL holder, battery connector (PP3 type) wire, solder, etc.

PWM Motor Controller

This circuit acts as a speed control for a 12 volt D.C. motor that draws a maximum current of up to one amp (or two amps if a suitably hefty power supply is used). It is primarily intended for use with a model train, but it no doubt has other possible uses. Simply feeding it from a variable voltage supply will provide control over the speed of a D.C. motor, but this does not give the ultimate in speed control. Much better results are obtained using a pulsed drive signal, and the waveforms of Figure 3.13 show how this system functions. The top waveform is a 1:1 squarewave, and the 12-volt output signal is therefore switched on for 50 percent of the time, and switched off for the other 50 percent. The average output voltage is therefore half the 12-volt peak amplitude of the output signal, or 6 volts in other words. In the middle waveform the output frequency is the same as before, but the output is at 12 volts for a much smaller percentage of the time. In fact the mark-space ratio is 1:5, and the output is at 12 volts for just one sixth of the time. This gives an average output potential equal to one sixth of 12 volts, which is obviously 2 volts. In the bottom waveform the output is at the 12-volt level for the majority of the time, and the mark-space ratio is 5:1. The output is at 12 volts for five sixths of the time, and the average output voltage is therefore 10 volts (i.e. five sixths of 12 volts).

It should be apparent from this that any average output voltage between zero and 12 volts can be obtained by using a signal having the appropriate mark-space ratio. Although one might expect the electric motor to object to a pulsed supply, there are usually no problems provided the output frequency is not very low or very high. With a low frequency of just a few

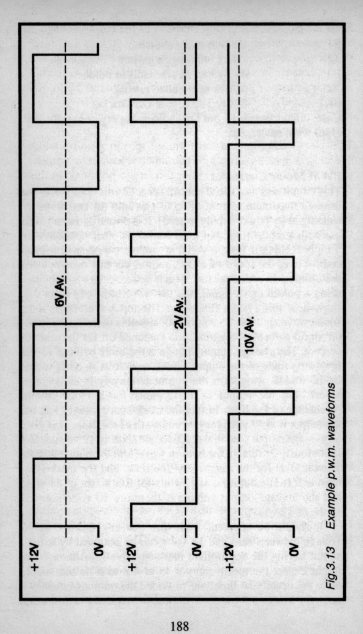

+12V

0V

6V Av.

+12V

0V

2V Av.

+12V

0V

10V Av.

Fig.3.13   Example p.w.m. waveforms

hertz the motor tends to stop and start as the output voltage is switched on and off. With a high frequency there is a problem of radio interference being radiated from the output wiring, and the inductance of the motor might be too high to permit adequate currents to flow. A frequency of around 50 to 500 hertz is usually satisfactory.

Circuit Operation

The circuit functions as a form of p.w.m. (pulse width modulator), which converts a D.C. input voltage into a pulsed output signal having a proportional average potential. In this case the input signal is from the speed control potentiometer, although a more complex voltage generator circuit can be used, as described at the end of this section. The circuit diagram for the p.w.m. is shown in Figure 3.14, and the output amplifier circuit appears in Figure 3.15. The latter boosts the output voltage and current capabilities of the circuit to levels that enable small D.C. electric motors to be driven by the circuit. Figure 3.16 shows the circuit for a mains power supply unit that can handle output currents of up to one amp. The relatively high power requirements of electric motors usually renders battery operation uneconomic.

Taking the p.w.m. circuit first, an analogue to digital converter is required in this application, and the modulator is therefore based on a PIC 16C71. The wiper of speed control VR1 connects to the channel 0 input of IC1. In order to give accurate output waveforms and an adequate output frequency it is necessary to use a high clock frequency. In fact C1 and R1 set the clock frequency at something approaching the 4MHz maximum for the 16C71-04. IC2 is a small monolithic voltage regulator that provides the modulator circuit with a well-stabilised five-volt supply. The circuit as a whole operates from a 12-volt supply.

The output amplifier uses TR1 as a common emitter switching stage, which drives a second common emitter switch (TR2). R4 limits the drive current to TR2 to only about 7.5 milliamps, but this is adequate because TR2 is a Darlington power device. Its current gain is typically several thousand times, and even with this modest drive current it can handle output currents of one or two amps. D1 is a protection diode

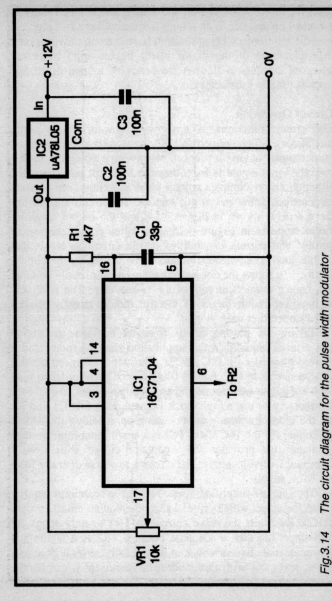

Fig.3.14   The circuit diagram for the pulse width modulator

190

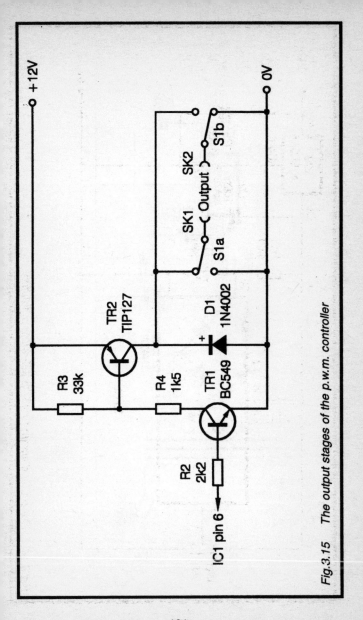

Fig.3.15   The output stages of the p.w.m. controller

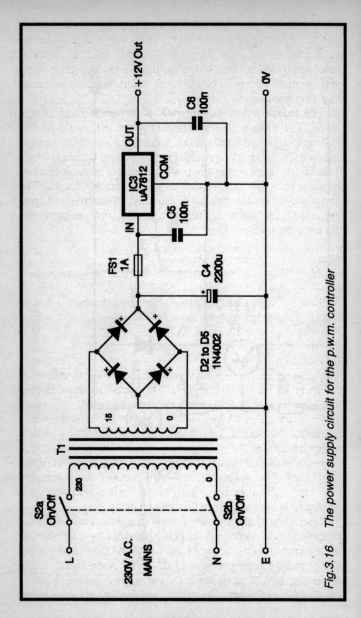

Fig.3.16   The power supply circuit for the p.w.m. controller

192

that suppresses any high voltage reverse polarity noise spikes that are generated across the highly inductive load provided by an electric motor. The direction of a D.C. electric motor is governed by the polarity of the supply. S1 enables the polarity of the output voltage to be changed, and it therefore functions as a direction control.

The mains power supply unit is a conventional design having full-wave bridge rectification provided by D2 to D5. The output is stabilised at 12 volts by monolithic voltage regulator IC3. This also provides output current limiting, which is an essential feature for the power supply as no form of over-current protection is included in the controller circuit. The power supply circuit should be able to handle currents of up to two amps if the following changes are made to the components, but the author has not tried this.

Component	Change Required
T1	Current rating must be 3.32 amps or more
D2 to D5	Change to 1N5402
FS1	Change to two amp current rating
C4	Change value to 4700u
IC3	Change to uA78S12

Inertia, Etc.
If the controller is to be used with model trains the modification of Figure 3.17 is very worthwhile. This gives simulated inertia, momentum, and braking. In other words, when the speed control is advanced it takes a short while for the train to actually respond to the change. This is rather like the 'real thing', where inertia results in the train pulling away slowly even if full power is used immediately. There is a similar delay when the speed control is backed off, and this simulates the momentum of a real train. Pressing a pushbutton switch that acts as a simulated brake can reduce this second delay.

Operation of the circuit is very straightforward, with the momentum and inertia effects being provided by a simple C-R timing circuit added between the output of the speed control (VR1) and the analogue input of IC1. VR1 is the speed control of the original circuit incidentally, but all the other components are all additional items. R5 and C7 are the timing components.

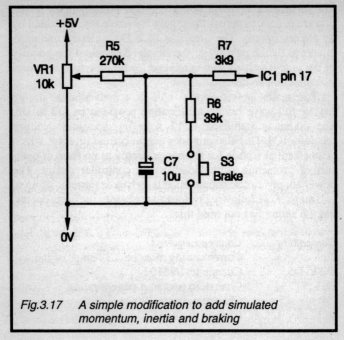

*Fig.3.17   A simple modification to add simulated
momentum, inertia and braking*

Operating S3 places R6 across C7 and this causes C7 to discharge more rapidly. Keeping S3 closed also tends to pull the input voltage to IC3 much lower, giving a lower speed than that set using VR1. This is much the same as the 'real thing', where applying the brake when the throttle was still well advanced would greatly slow down the train! With an electronic simulation this will not cause clouds of smoke from the wheels of the train, or cause and damage to the circuit, but it is not the correct way of driving the train.

As this circuit is mains powered it is essential that it is built to conform to the normal safety regulations. The case must be a metal type and it is essential that it is reliably earthed to the mains earth lead. Also, the case must be a type that has a screw-fitting lid, and not some form of clip-on lid or outer cover. This ensures that there is no easy means of gaining access to the dangerous mains wiring. Transistor TR2 controls quite high maximum currents, but due to its switching mode of operation it does not have to dissipate much power. Consequently, it does not require a large heatsink in order to prevent overheating. In fact it could probably work without a heatsink at all, but I would recommend 'playing safe' and fitting TR2 with a small clip-on or bolt-on TO220 type heatsink.

Software
The basic action of the software is to take a reading from the converter and then use this in two timing loops. After the initial setting up of the ports, etc., the main loop commences with a reading being taken from the converter. A check is then made to determine whether the reading is zero, because readings of FF or zero will cause a malfunction of the timing loops. If a reading of zero is detected, the program branches to the subprogram called 'OFF', where a delay loop is performed. The program then goes back to the beginning of the main loop and takes another reading from the converter.

Assuming a reading of more than zero is produced, the value from the converter 'HBYTE' and its complement is stored in 'LBYTE.' It is not essential for the output frequency of the controller to remain constant, but it is likely to work better if there are no major variations in the output frequency. Keeping the output frequency more or less constant is not difficult, and it is just a matter of making the low output period increase as the high output time decreases, and vice versa. The value from the converter controls the high output time, and its complement is used to set the low output time. The salient point here is that the two values always total FF (255 decimal), and as the value from the converter is increased, its complement therefore decreases. This gives the desired effect with a mark-space ratio that can be varied over a very wide range, and a constant output frequency. Although the control signal is an analogue one (the continuously variable voltage provided by VR1), the unit is essentially a digital circuit. The range of output powers is not infinite, and there are actually 255 speeds plus an off setting. However, there is no obvious stepping from one speed to the next and to the user the speed of the motor appears to be continuously variable.

Once the reading and its complement have been stored, a check is made to determine whether or not the complement is zero. If it is the program loops to 'ON', where the output is set high, held there briefly, and then set low again. With the speed control at maximum the output is not held continuously high, giving a small loss of power. At only around one percent this is not normally of any significance. In fact the voltage drop through TR2 is likely to be a more significant factor. A slightly higher supply voltage must be used for the p.w.m. circuit if it is important that the maximum output potential is a full 12 volts.

Assuming that the value from the converter is not either zero or FF, the program will reach the two timing loops. The output is set high, and then the first delay loop is performed. Then the output is set low, the second delay loop is performed, and the program then goes back to the beginning of the main loop. These are both two-stage loops, and it therefore takes many thousands of clock pulses to complete them both. The point of doing this is that it takes about 10 clock cycles to read the converter, store the value and its complement, etc. Using long timing loops ensures that the initial part of each loop does not significantly affect the timing of the output signal. This makes it essential to use a high clock frequency though, since the output frequency of the unit would otherwise be too low. The value in 'HBYTE' is used to control the number of loops in the first delay, and the value in 'LBYTE' controls the number of loops in the second delay.

```
;************************************************
;PWM Controller Program
;************************************************
;
STATUS      EQU         03
Z           EQU         02
BDIR        EQU         06
ADCON       EQU         08
PORTB       EQU         06
ADRES       EQU         09
LBYTE       EQU         0C
HBYTE       EQU         0D
CNTR        EQU         0F
CNTR2       EQU         10
```

196

```
          BSF       STATUS,5      ;Select page 1
          CLRF      BDIR          ;Set port B outputs
          MOVLW     02
          MOVWF     ADCON         ;Set RA0/1 as analogue inputs
          BCF       STATUS,5      ;Select page 0
          MOVLW     0xC1
          MOVWF     ADCON         ;Select Ch0/Internal clock
;
MAIN      BSF       ADCON,2       ;Start conversion
          NOP                     ;Wait
          MOVF      ADRES,0       ;Place conversion in W
          BTFSC     STATUS,Z
          GOTO      OFF
          MOVWF     HBYTE         ;Store reading
          MOVWF     LBYTE
          COMF      LBYTE,1       ;Store complement of reading
          BTFSC     STATUS,Z
          GOTO      ON
          BSF       PORTB,0       ;Set output high
LOOP1     MOVLW     10
          MOVWF     CNTR
HTIME     DECFSZ    CNTR,1
          GOTO      HTIME
          DECFSZ    HBYTE,1       ;Delay
          GOTO      LOOP1
          BCF       PORTB,0       ;Set output low
LOOP2     MOVLW     10
          MOVWF     CNTR
LTIME     DECFSZ    CNTR,1
          GOTO      LTIME
          DECFSZ    LBYTE,1
          GOTO      LOOP2
          GOTO      MAIN
;
OFF       MOVLW     20            ;Hold output low for a period
          MOVWF     CNTR2
          MOVLW     0xFF
          MOVWF     CNTR
OFFDEL    DECFSZ    CNTR,1
          GOTO      OFFDEL
```

```
          DECFSZ    CNTR2,1
          GOTO      OFFDEL
          GOTO      MAIN        ;Take new reading
;
ON        BSF       PORTB,0
          MOVLW     20          ;Hold output low for a period
          MOVWF     CNTR2
          MOVLW     0xFF
          MOVWF     CNTR
ONDEL     DECFSZ    CNTR,1
          GOTO      ONDEL
          DECFSZ    CNTR2,1
          GOTO      ONDEL
          BCF       PORTB,0
          GOTO      MAIN        ;Take new reading

          END
```

Components for P.W.M. Controller
(Figures 3.14, 3.15 and 3.16)

Resistors (all 0.25 watt 5% carbon film)
R1	4k7
R2	2k2
R3	33k
R4	1k5
R5	270k
R6	39k
R7	3k9

Potentiometer
VR1	10k lin carbon

Capacitors
C1	33p polystyrene
C2, C3, C5, C6	100n ceramic (4 off)
C4	2200µ 25V elect
C7	10µ 25V elect

198

Semiconductors

IC1	16C71-04
IC2	μA78L05 (+5V 100mA regulator)
IC3	μA7812 (+12V 1A regulator)
TR1	BC549
TR2	TIP127
D1 to D5	1N4002 (5 off)

Miscellaneous

T1	Standard mains primary, 0 - 15 volt 1.66A secondary
S1	d.p.d.t. toggle switch
S2	Rotary mains switch
S3	Push-to-make switch
FS1	20mm 1A 'quickblow' fuse

Metal case, circuit board, 20mm panel mounting fuse-holder, 18-pin DIL holder, control knob, TO220 heatsink, mains lead and plug, wire, solder, etc.

If the simulated momentum, inertia, and braking are needed, add R5, R6, R7, S3 and C7. See Figure 3.17.